LAS VEGAS TRIVIA

John Gollehon

GOLLEHON BOOKS™

GRAND RAPIDS, MICHIGAN

MANUFACTURED IN THE UNITED STATES OF AMERICA

Library of Congress Catalog Card Number 00-090774

ISBN 0-914839-54-3
(International Standard Book Number)

GOLLEHON is an exclusive trademark of Gollehon Press, Inc.

GOLLEHON BOOKS are published by: Gollehon Press, Inc.,
6157 28th St. SE, Grand Rapids, MI 49546.

GOLLEHON BOOKS are available in quantity purchases;
contact Special Sales. Gollehon does not accept unsolicited
manuscripts. Brief book proposals are reviewed.

Contents

Other Books Authored
By John Gollehon

Casino Games
Budget Gambling
The Confident Gambler
Conquering Casino Craps
What Casinos Don't Want You To Know
A Gambler's Bedside Reader
A Gambler's Little Instruction Book

The All About Series:
All About Blackjack
All About Craps
All About Slots And Video Poker
All About Roulette
All About Baccarat
All About Sports Betting
All About Keno

CHAPTER 1
Introduction

How To Play

- Before a question is asked, a player chooses either a 3-point or 5-point question. The 3-point questions are obviously the easiest. The player asking the question must choose the question at random and not review the question before asking.

- A correct answer to a multiple-choice question scores the points. There is no penalty for an incorrect answer. Whether or not a player answers the multiple-choice question correctly, he or she is entitled to the correct answer before being asked the bonus questions.

- Bonus and double bonus questions are always asked, but answering is optional. A player may decline without any penalty in score. However, should a player accept a bonus or double bonus question and answer incorrectly, the points are subtracted from the player's total score. The winning score is 21.

- The answers to the multiple-choice questions and both bonus questions are found on the following page, discreetly contained within a brief story-line paragraph. In this way, one cannot simply glance at the answers.

- The last chapter, "Fun Facts," is a section of randomly chosen facts that you can include in the game if you like, perhaps making up your own rules for their usage. Or, this section might be best left as just something fun to read.

The Changing Landscape

I've made a special effort in preparing the questions for *Las Vegas Trivia* to keep it as up-to-date as possible, no matter when you play it. We all know it's not much fun to be asked questions that have become obsolete.

There's only one way—and not a very good one—to ensure that *Las Vegas Trivia* never becomes outdated, and that's to base all of the questions on what historians call "first facts": Who was the first, what was the first, etc. No one can change a "first," but someone can always change a "largest." Las Vegas is a dynamic town. Change is the rule; not the exception. Whatever is the largest today—I guarantee you—will not be the largest tomorrow!

But all the questions can't be just firsts. Otherwise, *Las Vegas Trivia* would read like a history book. History is certainly an important part of *Las Vegas Trivia,* but there is so much more... lots of new things, so there are going to be some questions that are vulnerable to change. If you find an obsolete question, write to me. Fax me. Or send me an e-mail. Or use whatever new technology has made all the others obsolete.

I can only hope that the movers and shakers of Las Vegas pull up on the reins, at least a little, enough so that we can all catch our breath. Hotels are bought out by competitors and new names go up on the marquees. Streets are changed, games are changed, and the skyline changes with every new "larger" hotel.

Monopoly doesn't belong in Atlantic City; it belongs in Vegas! That's where all the buying and selling is going on!

My fear, as I wrestle with these questions, is that someone is going to come along with a few billion dollars and buy up a few hotels, screwing up a dozen or so of my hard-thought questions in one fell swoop! Well, guess what? That's exactly what happened! And I'm already on question number 120! I won't be able to wait to see if any of the hotels will change its name, or whether any of them will be "imploded" so that a "larger" hotel can be built. The presses are waiting. And I'm almost ready to send off the manuscript, assuming the technology for printing books doesn't change before it gets there.

Someday—I'm sure—I'll read in the newspaper that such-and-such conglomerate bought out the such-and-such conglomerate that owns Caesars Palace and, well, the name's getting old, says the new owners, and a new name is just the ticket. The old name comes down, the new name goes up: Bob's Bingo Palace.

If that ever happens, I quit.

Nostalgia

Nostalgia seems to be making a comeback. And what better city to show off its past than Las Vegas.

Sure, I know, Las Vegas is not history-book stuff. George Washington never slept there, Paul Revere never rode down its streets, there were no Civil War battles, not even an honest-to-gosh Indian war, no Industrial Revolution, no famous explorers... save one.... Mr. John C. Fremont, and he's probably the only Vegas connection you'll find in an 8th grade history book.

But believe this: The rich, storied past of Las Vegas is just as exciting as its present-day surprises, and its anything-can-happen future to come. But like I said, *Las Vegas Trivia* isn't just all "old stuff," as my young editor on staff likes to call it. There's new stuff, too. And there's neat stuff about casino games, and the attractions of Las Vegas beyond the glitz, from the Grand Canyon to Hoover Dam to Death Valley.

It's a great city! But I want you to know, especially those of you who are just now experiencing Las Vegas for the first time, that it has been many different cities, evolving from one into the other. It not only *is* a great city, it *was* a great city.

Perhaps some of you are lucky enough to have lived in Las Vegas in the '40s, for example, and to have watched the Los Angeles Highway (now the Strip) fill up with resorts. What would it have been like to be able to stand in front of the El Rancho Vegas, to look down the highway and see only a few small clubs?

Let's walk the highway together. The Sahara will be built right across the street. Over there will soon be the Frontier, and later the Desert Inn across the road. The Thunderbird will rise, and even farther down the road will come the infamous Flamingo, but it will take many years before it watches its new neighbor,

Caesars Palace, redefine "plush." And the MGM Grand and Luxor, and the Bellagio and Venetian, and Paris Las Vegas and New York-New York. But wait a minute. We're moving too fast. It's just sand now... and the mountains, and one lonely hotel.

Stand anywhere on the Strip today and if you feel as I do, you'll picture the old El Rancho Vegas standing somewhere else, many miles away, on a *different* road. A road that has been lost somewhere in time.

Remnants

Proof of the resurgence in our interest of the past is the mushrooming industry of antiques and collectibles. And Las Vegas is no exception. Chips, ashtrays, menus, photographs, postcards, what-have-you, from the earliest casinos can fetch big bucks! Collecting Las Vegas is fun. What a great way to connect with the past. And that's the title of our new Gollehon book I'm sure you'll enjoy. *Collecting Las Vegas* is a book you'll want to own.

We live in a time now when things move so fast that we barely have time to slow down and remember the good times. The motivational gurus, in their pep talks and book signings, tell us to live for the future. The past is history, they say. Your future, particularly your *financial* future, is all you should really think about. You must hurry, they say. You must hurry to your future.

Bunk! I say. If we forget our past, we forget who we really are.

CHAPTER 2

The Quiz Show

Q 1—5 pts. In the 1960 Frank Sinatra film, "Ocean's 11," which of the following casinos was *not* a target of the heist?

A: The Sahara   B: The Dunes
C: The Riviera   D: The Flamingo

Bonus Q—3 pts. Who played Duke Santos in this famous film?

Double Bonus Q—6 pts. During what season was the film shot? Hint: It only seemed as if it were beginning to look a lot like Christmas.

Q 2—3 pts. Elvis Presley's "comeback" performance in Las Vegas was in 1969 at the hotel now known as the Las Vegas Hilton. What was the name of this famous hotel at the time?

A: The Paradise   B: The Continental
C: The International   D: The Desert Palace

Bonus Q—2 pts. In what year did the hotel change its name? Hint: It was seven years before "The King" passed away.

Double Bonus Q—4 pts. At what hotel did Elvis *first* perform in Las Vegas?

A 1. Believe it or not, the plan was to blow up the electrical towers feeding power to Las Vegas. When all the lights would go out, and before backup power could be generated, Danny Ocean and his "rat pack" would clean out the vaults of the Sahara, Sands, Riviera, Desert Inn, and Flamingo hotels. "Ocean's 11" starred Frank Sinatra, Dean Martin, Sammy Davis Jr., Joey Bishop, Peter Lawford, and Cesar Romero. The latter played Las Vegas gangster Duke Santos. The movie was set during the holidays but was filmed during the summer. While the movie was being shot, summer vacationers to Las Vegas were wondering why there were Christmas decorations all over town.

A 2. Kirk Kerkorian built the International Hotel in 1969, which would become the Las Vegas Hilton in 1970, where Elvis would continue to wow his fans in SRO performances. Elvis first played Vegas at the New Frontier in 1956, but, surprisingly, his show was not exactly overrun by fans. After only one week of a two-week engagement, Elvis got the boot. This great entertainer was only at the forefront of his career.

Q 3—5 pts. In 1990, The Flamingo Hilton removed what last original vestige of gangster Benjamin "Bugsy" Siegel?

A: His bullet-ridden car   B: His rose garden
C: His original bar   D: His secret vault

Bonus Q—3 pts. What two other prominent mobsters joined in with Siegel to buy controlling interest in the Flamingo?

Double Bonus Q—6 pts. The Flamingo opened on December 26, 1946, only to close fewer than 30 days later due to financial losses. When it reopened March 1, 1947, what new name did Bugsy give it?

Q 4—5 pts. Legendary billionaire Howard Hughes set up living quarters on an entire floor in the penthouse suites of what famous Strip hotel?

A: The Frontier   B: The MGM Grand
C: The Desert Inn   D: The Stardust

Bonus Q—3 pts. Hughes died during a flight from Acapulco to the United States for urgent medical treatment. To what city was he headed?

Double Bonus Q—6 pts. Hughes' real estate holdings, including several Las Vegas hotels, were managed for many years after his death by what famous-name corporation?

A 3. The Flamingo was a land-locked property, and space was at a premium during massive remodeling during the '90s. From Bugsy's days, one of the last remnants to bite the dust was his famous rose garden, which he designed and tended by himself. An argument could be made that his original penthouse survived until 1993, but it had undergone renovation beforehand and hardly resembled its original state at the time of demolition. Siegel teamed up with Meyer Lansky and Frank Costello to finish the plans of the actual founder, Billy Wilkerson, who had started the project but ran out of funds.

A 4. Rumor has it that Hughes enjoyed his stay at the Desert Inn so much that he wanted to buy the hotel. But the truth is, the hotel wanted him out because they needed the rooms. Hughes solved his dilemma by simply buying the hotel. He lived on the entire 5th floor for nearly four years. He would later buy or build seven more hotels in Las Vegas, including the Landmark, the Frontier, the Silver Slipper, the Sands, and the Castaways, all properties of his Summa Corporation. This eccentric mogul became seriously ill in 1976 and was rushed to a specialist in Houston, Texas, but he died during the flight.

Q 5—3 pts. What engineering marvel propelled Las Vegas into a boomtown, more than doubling the population almost overnight?

A: Boulder Dam   **B:** The Grand Canyon
C: Railroads   **D:** Nuclear Test Site

Bonus Q—2 pts. In what year did this rapid growth begin?

Double Bonus Q—4 pts. What other notable event occurred in Nevada during that same year?

Q 6—3 pts. Before the Las Vegas Strip became home to the most luxurious gambling palaces in the world, what street in Las Vegas served up the games in the best Wild West tradition?

A: Paradise Road   **B:** Las Vegas Blvd.
C: Fremont St.   **D:** Boulder Highway

Bonus Q—2 pts. What was the first "high-rise" hotel on this famous street?

Double Bonus Q—4 pts. Today, what chintzy name is this street still trying to shake?

A 5. Although the railroads brought plenty of
workers to Las Vegas in 1904, it was the construction
of Boulder Dam (now Hoover Dam), that put Las
Vegas on the map. The year was 1931, during the
Great Depression, when literally thousands of unem-
ployed men journeyed to this whistle-stop in the
desert, only to be turned away because the jobs were
already taken. During that same year, gambling
became legalized in Nevada, and, although not exactly
a "notable event," divorce laws were relaxed. You
could lose your money, and your honey, at the same
time.

A 6. During the rapid growth years of the '30s,
Fremont Street in downtown Las Vegas was the place
to be. Hotel rooms were almost always full, with
tourists flocking to Las Vegas to see Boulder Dam
and to swim in Lake Mead, which the dam created. It
was also a chance to experience the last of the frontier
towns, complete with faro games, bordellos, and real
saloons. It wasn't until the 15-story Fremont Hotel
opened in the mid '50s that downtown Las Vegas
began to lose its Wild West ambiance and turn into
what has affectionately been dubbed, Glitter Gulch.

Q 7—5 pts. You're sitting at a roulette wheel, playing the "inside" numbers. The ball drops, the dealer puts the marker on No. 29, right on top of your $5 chip! Voilà! Your number hit! So how much did you win?

   A: $150   **B:** $175
   C: $185   **D:** $90

Bonus Q—3 pts. Assuming that the wheel has both a single zero and double zero, as most have, how much should you have been paid if the game were fair?

Double Bonus Q—6 pts. What is the house percentage on the bet you just made?

Q 8—3 pts. At the blackjack table, you can't understand why a pit boss stops the game and tells the dealer to shuffle before the cut-card has appeared. What is the most likely reason for this "premature shuffle"?

   A: A misdeal   **B:** A bent card
   C: Dealer change   **D:** Suspected card-counter

Bonus Q—2 pts. How long does it take for a good dealer to shuffle eight decks of cards?

Double Bonus Q—4 pts. What is the new way to shuffle cards?

A 7. I purposely said that the marker was placed on top of your chip, meaning that your chip was on one number, not straddling a line, which constitutes a bet of more than one number. One-number bets pay off at 35 to 1 odds, so you won $175 ($5 times 35). Since there are 38 different compartments where the ball might land, the correct odds of winning are 37 to 1. In a fair game, you would win $185. The difference is the house edge: The $10 the house shorted you, divided by $190 (all 38 wagers at $5 a pop), is 5.26 percent, the house advantage.

A 8. Whenever you see a dealer "shuffle-up," it almost always means that a pit boss suspects a card-counter is at the table, *and,* the count is running against the house. Shuffles are the bane of casino operators. Why? Because in the four minutes it takes to shuffle eight decks, three or four rounds can be dealt to a full table. That's why more and more casinos are installing automatic shuffling machines. When one shoe is finished, a fresh shoe is ready to go. An exceptional dealer can cut that four minutes to three, so anywhere from three to four minutes is an acceptable answer.

Q 9—5 pts. Which of the following place-bets gives the player the lowest house percentage at the craps tables?

A: 6 or 8   **B:** 5 or 9
C: 4 or 10   **D:** All are the same

Bonus Q—3 pts. What is the house percentage on this best set of place-bets?

Double Bonus Q—6 pts. If you make a place-bet on 6, what are the odds you'll roll the six before you roll a 7?

Q 10—3 pts. Which of the following casino games gives a player the best chance of winning, over the long term?

A: Craps   **B:** Roulette
C: Slots   **D:** Poker

Bonus Q—2 pts. What casino table-game is most often mispronounced?

Double Bonus Q—4 pts. What casino game is often played by minors, even though it is illegal for under-age players to engage in gambling?

A 9. Astute dice players know that only the 6 or 8 place-bets are worth betting. The house takes a fairly small cut on these bets—about one and one-half percent. The other place-bets are considerably higher. Since there are five ways to roll a 6, and six ways to roll a 7, the odds of winning the bet are 6 to 5.

A 10. Hands down, it's poker—the live game, not the video version. Poker players are not playing against the house as is the case in all other casino games; they are competing against the skill of the other players, not to mention a modest "rake" by the casino as a percentage cost for operating the game. The casinos' most elite game, baccarat, is pronounced "Bah'-cah-rah." If you call it "Back'-a-rat," you're giving yourself away as a rank novice. It's not unusual for moms and dads who bring their kids to Vegas to let them play keno in the casino's restaurants. The casino doesn't mind if kids fill out the tickets, but a parent must pay for any tickets played.

TIDBIT—Bugsy Siegel, the Flamingo Hotel's famous owner, thought "them pink birds" were called "flemencos."

Q 11—3 pts. Which of the following casino games produces the most decisions per hour?

A: Craps   **B:** Roulette
C: Slots   **D:** Blackjack

Bonus Q—2 pts. What is a "negative-expectation" game?

Double Bonus Q—4 pts. What game has the unique trait of providing both negative and positive expectations?

Q 12—3 pts. What bet wins when the "stickperson" at a craps table says, "Pay the line"?

A: Field   **B:** Pass
C: Don't Pass   **D:** Come

Bonus Q—2 pts. In what direction do the dice pass around a craps table as different players become the shooter?

Double Bonus Q—4 pts. What event at the dice table causes a player shooting the dice to have to pass the dice to the next player who becomes the next shooter?

A 11. With the advent of "credit-play" in the early '90s, slot machines became the most prolific money-makers for casinos by increasing the frequency of play. Players no longer needed to insert coin after coin for each play; the simple push of a button would play "maximum coins," which players most often must do to win the top jackpot. All slot machines are negative-expectation games, which means the house has a built-in edge. The longer you play, the more likely you will lose. Unlike all other casino games, blackjack offers occasional positive expectations. But you must count the played cards in order to tell when the edge has swung to your favor.

A 12. The stickperson, one of the dealers armed with a curved stick to retrieve and deliver the dice to a shooter, also announces the rolls of the dice. *Pay the line* means that the pass-line won. It's called a *pass*. Everyone who was betting "the front line" wins. The dice travel around the table in a clockwise direction. A shooter keeps the dice until a "seven-out," which means a 7 was rolled before a point-number was repeated.

Q 13—3 pts. What is the generally accepted Spanish translation of the name *Las Vegas?*

  A: The valley   **B:** The desert
  C: The springs   **D:** The meadows

Bonus Q—2 pts. What first attracted Indians to settle in the valley now known as Las Vegas?

Double Bonus Q—4 pts. Name the Indian tribe first to establish a settlement in the Las Vegas Valley.

Q 14—3 pts. In what desert is Las Vegas situated?

  A: The Mojave   **B:** The Gobi
  C: The Sahara   **D:** The Great Victoria

Bonus Q—2 pts. Where does Nevada rank in terms of annual rainfall?

Double Bonus Q—4 pts. Where does Las Vegas get its water? Hint: It's also the source of its power.

A 13. The name *Las Vegas* means "the meadows" in Spanish. In fact, the valley was an oasis in the desert, providing spring water for the Anasazi Indians, who first inhabited the area. The Anasazi tribe was forced out of the valley more than a thousand years ago by the Paiute Indians.

A 14. Las Vegas is surrounded by the Mohave Desert, which contributes greatly to Nevada's claim of being the state with the lowest annual rainfall, barely more than eight inches per year. Desert springs abound, but certainly cannot provide the water to quench one of the United States' fastest growing cities. The damming of the great Colorado River in 1931 with the creation of Boulder Dam continues to provide water and electrical power to Las Vegas, although the limits of both are now sorely tested.

TIDBIT—The biggest dealer tip ever made was $120,000! The player who tipped won over $2 million!

Q 15—5 pts. What nearby National Monument is the lowest elevation in the United States?

  A: Death Valley   **B:** The Grand Canyon
  C: Red Rock Canyon   **D:** Valley of Fire

Bonus Q—3 pts. What two nearby national parks are located in Utah?

Double Bonus Q—6 pts. What nearby National Conservation Area, just a short drive from the famed Las Vegas Strip, provides spectacular sandstone formations as part of an ancient sea?

Q 16—3 pts. In what part of Nevada is Las Vegas located?

  A: North   **B:** South
  C: East   **D:** West

Bonus Q—2 pts. Name the major nearby market for Las Vegas gamblers.

Double Bonus Q—4 pts. Name the five states that border Nevada.

A 15.

A popular tourist attraction skirting the Nevada/California border is Death Valley, the lowest point in the United States at 282 feet below sea level. As you might imagine, the hottest temperatures are routinely recorded there in the summer, although winter daytime temperatures might only be in the 50s. Death Valley is one of the premier spots to view the most spectacular sunsets. Las Vegas is blessed with nearby tourist attractions, including Zion and Bryce Canyon National Parks in Utah. Closer to Las Vegas, Red Rock Canyon is a must-see for weary-eyed gamblers who need a break from the action. The serene landscape offers contrasting solitude to relax and recharge your batteries.

A 16.

Las Vegas is situated in the southern tip of the state, only four or five hours by car from its principal player market, Southern California. Note: "California" is not an acceptable answer. The five states that surround Nevada are: Oregon and Idaho on the north, Utah and Arizona on the east, and California on the west. Technically, there is no southern border state because of Nevada's pointed shape to the south.

Q 17—3 pts. Other than gambling, what draws the most visitors to Las Vegas?

A: The shows   **B:** The Grand Canyon
C: Conventions   **D:** Shopping

Bonus Q—2 pts. What is the name of the airport that serves Las Vegas?

Double Bonus Q—4 pts. What is the least busiest time to visit Las Vegas?

Q 18—5 pts. What Las Vegas hotel had the dubious honor of being the first to book topless showgirls? Hint: The hotel was "imploded" in 1992.

A: The Landmark   **B:** The Aladdin
C: The Dunes   **D:** The Hacienda

Bonus Q—3 pts. What Las Vegas "connection" do Bruce Willis and Demi Moore, Richard Gere and Cindy Crawford, and Elvis and Priscilla Presley all have in common?

Double Bonus Q—6 pts. Name the only U.S. president to perform at a Las Vegas hotel.

A 17. Although some surveys have indicated that "shopping" is the number-one reason cited by visitors, the convention business is clearly the correct answer. Many of the country's largest trade shows can only set up in Las Vegas because no other city can provide enough hotel rooms for all those who attend. Nearly half of all visitors arrive by plane at McCarran International Airport. If you don't like crowds, plan your trip between Thanksgiving and Christmas, the slowest time of the year in Las Vegas. Another suggestion: Avoid the weekends.

A 18. Today it's no big deal, but in the '50s, it was headline news when the Dunes Hotel filled its showroom stage with bare-breasted dancers. Although the Dunes opened in 1955 to modest success, it was on that day in 1957 that things really started to take off. Yes, Las Vegas is the entertainment capital of the world, and maybe the marriage capital, too. That's right. Bruce and Demi, and all the rest, said their "I do's" in Vegas. Ronald Reagan was on the bill at the Last Frontier in 1954.

Q 19—5 pts. What is the right move at a black-jack table if you have 14 (a pair of 7s) and the dealer has 8?

  A: Stand   **B:** Hit
  C: Double   **D:** Split

Bonus Q—3 pts. What two paired values are always split?

Double Bonus Q—6 pts. What paired value is always hit?

Q 20—5 pts. What bet at the roulette table is worse than all the others?

  A: 3-number bet   **B:** 4-number bet
  C: 5-number bet   **D:** 6-number bet

Bonus Q—3 pts. What direction does the roulette wheel turn? What direction does the ball spin? (Both questions must be answered correctly.)

Double Bonus Q—6 pts. Other than a red number alternating with a black number, name one other "intelligent" aspect of the wheel-numbering system.

A 19. Most beginners have trouble with pairs, but if you remember basic rules, it isn't so tough. Only split a 14 if the dealer has 7 or less. With an 8 showing, it's too risky to split because the dealer might have 18, and splitting the 7s most likely will leave you with 17s or worse. The correct answer is, to hit. Always split aces and 8s. Always hit a pair of 4s.

A 20. All the bets at roulette, except one, give the house a 5.26 percent advantage. But the 5-number bet (0, 00, 1, 2, and 3) costs you 7.89 percent. The wheel turns counterclockwise; the ball spins clockwise. A pair of even numbers alternates with a pair of odd numbers; odd numbers are directly opposite the next-highest even number; adjacent same-color numbers total 37. There are exceptions near the green numbers.

TIDBIT—Frank Sinatra made his debut in Las Vegas in 1951 at the Desert Inn.

Q 21—3 pts. How many 10-value cards are there in an eight-deck shoe at the blackjack table?

A: 32 **B:** 24

C: 40 **D:** 80

Bonus Q—2 pts. What is the best number of decks to play against if you are a blackjack card-counter?

Double Bonus Q—4 pts. Typically, how many decks are cut (taken out of play) in an eight-deck blackjack shoe?

Q 22—3 pts. You can always tell the coin denomination of a slot machine by the color of the "candle" on top of the machine. What color is the candle on a dollar machine?

A: Blue **B:** Red

C: Yellow **D:** Orange

Bonus Q—2 pts. 6 pts. What is the most popular coin denomination for slot machines on the Strip in Las Vegas?

Double Bonus Q—4 pts. What is the most popular coin denomination for slot machines in downtown Las Vegas?

A 21. There are four 10-value cards per deck: the 10, jack, queen, and king. So, there are 32 10-value cards in the shoe. The more that remain in the unplayed decks, the better for you. Fewer decks are easier to count, which means figuring out when there are more or fewer 10-value cards remaining than the normal expectancy. One deck is the best for counting, two decks aren't bad, but six or more are very difficult to count down. Dealers today generally cut from one and one-half to two full decks out of play. (Either answer is acceptable.) Card-counters are looking for weak cut-card penetration so that more cards can be counted.

A 22. Dollar machines have a blue candle on top, and are the most popular machines to play on the Strip; but in downtown Las Vegas, quarter machines are still the machines of choice for the majority of players.

TIDBIT—The Fiesta, the first hotel-casino in North Las Vegas, opened in 1994.

Q 23—5 pts. What is the oldest symbol still used on slot machines today?

A: Cherries   B: Bars
C: Bells   D: Sevens

Bonus Q—3 pts. Name either of the two most popular manufacturers of slot machines today.

Double Bonus Q—6 pts. Name either of the two most popular manufacturers of slot machines from the 1930s to the '60s.

Q 24—5 pts. On a video poker machine, the payouts for what two poker hands usually determine the percentage of the machine?

A: 3 of a kind/straight   B: Straight/flush
C: 2 pair/3 of a kind   D: Flush/full house

Bonus Q—3 pts. Name the company that developed the first successful line of video slot machines.

Double Bonus Q—6 pts. Name the company widely credited with designing and marketing video poker machines much as they are today.

A 23. Although horseshoes and stars, not to mention pictures of playing cards, were popular symbols during the slot machine's infancy, the symbol widely credited as having survived well over a hundred years of changes is the bell. Most often, the symbol is in yellow and depicts the Liberty Bell in Independence Hall in Philadelphia. Mills and Jennings are two manufacturers that were perhaps the most innovative in slot machine design and features. Today, Bally Manufacturing and International Game Technology (IGT) are perhaps best-known and provide the lion's share of machines to casinos everywhere.

A 24. Payouts for the flush and full house are the telltale signs you need to look for on the machine's paytables. Most often, a 6-9 machine (paying 6 coins for a flush and 9 coins for a full house) is the best paytable you can find. Although 5-6 and 5-8 payouts are also popular, they are obviously not as good. In the early '70s, Fortune Coin Company pioneered video gaming machines, but after a buy-out by Sircoma, the forerunner to International Game Technology, it was indeed IGT who led the way to market with many of the same features we still see today.

Q 25—5 pts. Las Vegas is situated in Clark County. What person is Clark County named after?

  A: Dr. Milo Clark   **B:** Clark Kent
  C: Gov. John Clark   **D:** Sen. William Clark

Bonus Q—3 pts. In what year was Las Vegas founded?

Double Bonus Q—6 pts. What industry helped Las Vegas grow in those early years?

Q 26—5 pts. What was the first hotel/casino to be built on what would become the Las Vegas Strip?

  A: The El Rancho Vegas **B:** The Last Frontier
  C: The Thunderbird   **D:** The Flamingo

Bonus Q—3 pts. Name the year that this exciting new resort opened.

Double Bonus Q—6 pts. Across from what existing Strip hotel was it located?

TIDBIT—Thanks to its popular buffet, Circus Circus serves more meals than any other hotel in the world... nearly 13,000 per day!

A 25. A politician holding many county jobs before his election to Congress, Senator William Clark is the namesake of Clark County. Even before its founding in 1905, Las Vegas prospered as a railroad town, until the building of Boulder Dam signaled a new economy for Las Vegas.

A 26. Most people think it's the Flamingo, but that's not even close. The very first hotel/casino built on what is now the Las Vegas Strip was the El Rancho Vegas. There were several "clubs" on the road before the El Rancho Vegas was built in 1941, but that's all they were... no hotel rooms, no "resort" atmosphere, no "casino" ambience. Today, if you want to see where the famed El Rancho Vegas stood, you must walk across the Strip from the Sahara Hotel.

TIDBIT—The Desert Inn Road arterial was completed in 1996, becoming the first tunnel under the Las Vegas Strip.

Q 27

—5 pts. Name the second resort hotel/casino to be built nearby on the same highway two years later.

A: The Desert Inn   **B:** The Last Frontier
C: The Thunderbird   **D:** The Flamingo

Bonus Q—3 pts. This is the same hotel that has been plagued by three different, but similar, names. What are they?

Double Bonus Q—6 pts. Three years later, another "fabulous" resort opens on this budding highway, farther to the south. Can you name it?

Q 28

—3 pts. What is the official name of what we all refer to as the Las Vegas Strip?

A: Nevada Blvd.   **B:** Las Vegas Blvd.
C: Clark Road   **D:** Fremont St.

Bonus Q—2 pts. What was it known as before it became a Strip of world-class hotel/casinos?

Double Bonus Q—4 pts. Before the resorts were built, most locals referred to the road by its route name. What was its highway designation?

A 27. A guest staying at the El Rancho Vegas, R. E. Griffith, couldn't help but notice its incredible success. So this owner of a string of Texas theaters quickly bought some land to the south and built The Last Frontier in 1943. The name was changed to The New Frontier in 1955, following a grand remodeling. Then, in 1967, this venerable hotel became known simply as The Frontier. In 1946, the third major resort opened on this highway... you guessed it... The Flamingo.

A 28. If you mail a letter to any of the casinos on the Strip, the address is Las Vegas Blvd. When only a handful of resorts dotted the road in the 1940s, it was known as the Los Angeles Highway... and for good reason: It led straight to Los Angeles. But locals knew it as U.S. 91. In fact, several businesses picked up on the name, including the 91 Club, a modest bar and casino located where the Last Frontier would be built.

TIDBIT—Las Vegas-style gambling hit California Indian casinos in 2000 with the passage of a state-wide referendum.

Q 29—5 pts. During the '40s, what other major development, in addition to casino gambling, would bring more people to Las Vegas?

A: Hoover Dam   **B:** Military installation
C: Nuclear testing   **D:** Silver mining

Bonus Q—3 pts. The flashy resorts of the '40s brought top-name entertainment to Las Vegas. In 1944, "Mr. Showmanship" made his Las Vegas debut at the Last Frontier and would later become a Las Vegas icon. Can you name him? Hint: His brother's name was George.

Double Bonus Q—6 pts. Another top performer would open at the El Rancho Vegas in 1945, later to become a member of Sinatra's "Rat Pack." Hint: If you can't answer this question, the Candy Man can.

Q 30—5 pts. What famous film star lost his wife, Carole Lombard, in a plane crash while waiting for her to join him at the El Rancho Vegas resort.

A: Clark Gable   **B:** W. C. Fields
C: Gene Autry   **D:** Glenn Ford

Bonus Q—3 pts. Name the adorning trademark that sat high atop the El Rancho Vegas? Hint: The large blades were outlined in neon, offering a dramatic guidepost to travelers against the black, desert nights.

Double Bonus Q—6 pts. The El Rancho Vegas resort would become known as the "Gateway to the Stars." But it's gone now. What happened to it?

A 29. World War II would usher in several new military installations across the country, including a strategic air field north of Las Vegas, called Las Vegas Army Air Field. It would grow exponentially to become Nellis Air Force Base, virtually a city within itself. Even while the war was going on, Las Vegas continued to earn a deserving reputation for top entertainment. No one could hold a candle (even a candelabra) to Mr. Entertainment. That's right: Liberace. And Sammy Davis Jr. was making inroads for his career, if not for civil rights causes, which would come later. The great Candy Man himself had to enter and leave the hotel in the back, through the kitchen.

A 30. Because it was the first plush resort in Las Vegas, The El Rancho Vegas lured many famous names from Hollywood. It was Clark Gable who was given the tragic news of his wife's death en route to Vegas. The El Rancho Vegas' famous trademark was a windmill. Sadly, the El Rancho Vegas burned to the ground in a suspicious early-morning fire on June 17, 1960. It was not rebuilt.

Q 31—3 pts. What direction are you walking if you are in front of Bally's on the Strip and heading toward the MGM Grand?

A: East   **B:** South
C: North   **D:** West

Bonus Q—2 pts. Speaking of the MGM Grand, what hotel did it displace when it was built on the corner of Tropicana Avenue in 1993?

Double Bonus Q—4 pts. But there was an MGM Grand before 1993. Indeed there was. Where was the original MGM Grand located?

Q 32—3 pts. What catastrophe at the original MGM Grand in 1980, and months later at the Las Vegas Hilton, caused Las Vegas to rethink its building codes for high-rise hotels?

A: Flood   **B:** Bombing
C: Fire   **D:** Airplane crash

Bonus Q—2 pts. What is the MGM Grand named after?

Double Bonus Q—4 pts. Who opened the original MGM Grand showroom? Name the showroom? Hint: He loved to roast "celebrities."

A 31. It's important to note where you are on the Strip, because it makes a bend near the Venetian, which few visitors realize. It explains why many people get "turned around" on the Strip. But the intersection of the Strip and Flamingo Road, where Bally's is located, makes perfect compass points. Looking down toward the MGM Grand is directly south. Many visitors think it's east. The "new" MGM Grand devoured the old Marina Hotel and the Tropicana's traditional golf course. Bally's, incidentally, is the original MGM Grand, built in 1973.

A 32. A fire raced through the hotel early in the morning of November 21, 1980, claiming 85 lives. The enormous casino was completely gutted in seconds. The MGM Grand is named after the 1932 movie, Grand Hotel. For many years after its gala opening, it would seem as if Dean Martin's name was always on the marquee, playing the room he opened: the famous Celebrity Room.

TIDBIT—Sports betting in Las Vegas sports books exceeds $2 billion a year. Over $70 million alone is wagered on the Super Bowl.

Q 33—3 pts. Which of the following hotels is not one of the corner hotels at the Strip and Flamingo Road?

A: Caesars Palace   **B:** Bally's
C: The Flamingo   **D:** Barbary Coast

Bonus Q—2 pts. What hotel used to be one of the big four, located where the Bellagio now stands?

Double Bonus Q—4 pts. This famous corner used to be the busiest in the world. But not any longer. The title holder is still on the Strip, but at what intersection?

Q 34—3 pts. What hotel features a powerful beam of light ten miles high, emanating into the night sky from the top of a giant pyramid?

A: The MGM Grand   **B:** The Luxor
C: The Stratosphere   **D:** The Sahara

Bonus Q—2 pts. From what country is the hotel's name taken?

Double Bonus Q—4 pts. What marvel of construction has become this hotel's signature feature? Hint: It has become the most recognized face in Las Vegas.

A 33. If we're going to get technical about it, the four hotels are Caesars Palace, The Bellagio, Bally's, and Barbary Coast. The Flamingo is just off the corner. The Dunes Hotel had its footprint in the sand for 37 years before the Bellagio bullied it away, along with its legendary golf course. With mega-resorts taking every available square foot near the corner of the Strip and Tropicana Blvd., this is an area Driver's Ed teachers avoid!

A 34. Jet pilots claim they can see the Luxor's beam of light on a clear evening as far away as Los Angeles. The term *Luxor* refers to Al Uqsur, Egypt's most exotic tourist locale, on the banks of the Nile. A dramatic re-creation of the Sphinx, with the body of a lion and the head of a man, leaves guests awestruck as they enter the pyramid.

TIDBIT—The first hotel-casino in Summerlin, a growing community northwest of Las Vegas, became known as the Regent in 2000.

Q 35—3 pts. If you found a "Big Bertha" in Las Vegas, what did you find?

A: Golf course   **B:** Prostitute
C: Handgun   **D:** Slot machine

Bonus Q—2 pts. Where exactly would you find them when they first appeared on the scene?

Double Bonus Q—4 pts. Name any two interesting features about one?

Q 36—5 pts. What are you doing if you are "past-posting"?

A: Cheating   **B:** Betting over the maximum
C: Counting cards **D:** Playing a system

Bonus Q—3 pts. Where did the term come from?

Double Bonus Q—6 pts. What casino game is most often involved?

TIDBIT—The most ever paid for an acre of land along the Las Vegas Strip was $2 million!

A 35. A Big Bertha was a come-on, a huge slot machine, maybe seven feet tall, usually positioned right inside the entrance to a casino. In the old days, barkers on the sidewalk would pass out coupons for free pulls, just to get you inside. Crowds would always gather to watch the reels drop slowly into position, adding to the suspense. Most had four reels, and the symbols used were mostly fruit. But the jackpot symbols that rarely lined up were big, red 7s.

A 36. The term *past-posting,* a form of cheating, comes from the racetrack. In the days when race results were fed to off-track betting parlors over a wire, some bettors figured out how to delay the feed and make a bet on a race after it finished! The roulette table gets more past-posters than other games. One player distracts the dealer while signaling the winning number to another player who makes the bet.

TIDBIT—The legal age for gambling in Nevada is 21. If you are underage, and hit a big jackpot, you will *not* be paid.

Q 37—5 pts. In casino parlance, what does the term *juice* mean?

A: Electricity   B: Dealer tips
C: Liquor   D: The percentages

Bonus Q—3 pts. What other often-used terms mean the same thing? Name two.

Double Bonus Q—6 pts. In what gambling endeavor is this term more often heard?

Q 38—5 pts. In the casino's race book, what don't you like if you don't like the "prices"?

A: Program cost   B: Payoffs
C: Purse money   D: Program changes

Bonus Q—3 pts. What is an "overlay"?

Double Bonus Q—6 pts. What is meant by the expression, "Looking for the horse to beat the winner"?

A 37. The juice is what you're always fighting. It's the casino advantage, also called the house "PC," or simply "the percentages." At the racetrack, it's called the "take-out"; at a poker table, it's called a "rake"; at baccarat and sometimes at craps, it's called the "commission," although the game percentages are usually more than that. But in the sports book, the regulars almost always refer to the edge they're fighting as "juice."

A 38. The prices are the projected payoffs for a winning horse, which may also be expressed as odds. An overlay is a horse going off at higher odds (a better price to pay if it wins) than the odds listed in the program (an expert's educated guess). If you're "looking for the horse to beat the winner," it means you've found the horse you think will win, but you also think the price (your winnings) would be too low, so you look for another horse with a better price. It's not a very smart way to pick horses.

Q 39—5 pts. If you bet an "exacta" in the casino's race book, how many horses must you correctly call, and in what positions of finish?

  A: 1st & 2nd/exact order
  B: 1st & 2nd/either order
  C: 1st, 2nd & 3rd/exact order
  D: 1st, 2nd & 3rd/exact order

Bonus Q—3 pts. What are the terms used at the track for finishing 1st, 2nd, and 3rd?

Double Bonus Q—6 pts. What is the difference between an exacta and a "perfecta"?

Q 40—3 pts. Which of the following slot machines usually offer you the best chance to win?

  A: Mechanical Reels   **B:** Video Keno
  C: Video Poker   **D:** Video Reels

Bonus Q—2 pts. Name two important differences between a reel-type slot machine and a video poker machine?

Double Bonus Q—4 pts. What determines where the reels on today's slot machines will stop?

A 39. An exacta wager requires that you correctly pick the first- and second-place horse in exact order. The first-place finish is called *win;* second place is called *place,* and third place is called *show*. An exacta and a perfecta are the same bet. For some reason, most tracks in the Midwest prefer the term *perfecta*.

A 40. There's little argument among the experts: Video poker is the game to play. You can apply skill to this game, and you can shop for the best percentages displayed right on the screen. Just compare the payouts and choose the one paying out the most coins. Note especially the payouts for a flush, full house, and two pair. The reels are controlled by a computer chip, even on machines that look mechanical.

TIDBIT—The record slot machine jackpot is $34.9 million, won on Megabucks in 2000.

Q 41—3 pts. What are the odds of getting a "royal flush" on a video poker machine?

A: 40,000 to 1   **B:** 75,000 to 1
C: 100,000 to 1   **D:** 200,000 to 1

Bonus Q—2 pts. If you saw a player get a royal flush just minutes ago, what are the odds that this same player will get another one on the same machine?

Double Bonus Q—4 pts. Why does a royal flush pay so much more than a straight flush when it's just as hard to get *any* straight flush?

Q 42—5 pts. What is the correct action if you are dealt 10♥, 10♦, J♦, 9♦, 6♦?

A: Keep the 10s and draw 3.
B: Keep the 10♦ and J♦ and go for the royal.
C: Go for the flush and draw 1.
D: Keep the 9♦, 10♦, J♦ and go for the straight flush.

Bonus Q—3 pts. Which of the following is the higher hand: Flush, three-of-kind, or straight?

Double Bonus Q—6 pts. What is the difference between drawing for an "open end" straight and drawing for an "inside" straight?

A 41. Although the odds of getting a royal flush are about 40,000 to 1, casinos have found that the odds are actually less (about 32,000 to 1) for some players because they take more risk, throwing away smaller wins (such as a hand containing a pair of jacks and 3 to a royal—a king and queen suited to one of the jacks, for example) in pursuit of the top jackpot. Whether a player just hit a royal or not makes no difference to the odds as that person continues playing. Which machine is played makes no difference to the odds, either. The royal pays more than any other straight flush because the royal is only one of ten straight flushes possible.

A 42. You have a better chance, approximately one in four, of making the flush. A straight beats three-of-a-kind; a flush beats them both. Drawing to an open-end straight means that you hold four consecutive cards excluding an ace. You can make the straight by getting the right card at either end (drawing a 4 or 9, for example, when holding 5-6-7-8 makes the straight). Drawing to an inside straight means that only one card will "fill" the straight, such as drawing a 6 when holding 4-5-7-8. Some players refer to an inside straight as a "closed" straight.

Q 43—5 pts. At blackjack, what three pairs should never be split?

A: 4s, 5s, & 10s **B:** 2s, 3s, & 4s
C: 4s, 6s & 10s **D:** 6s, 7s, and 8s

Bonus Q—3 pts. Speaking of splitting pairs, what is the dumbest split a player can make?

Double Bonus Q—6 pts. In most casinos, what happens if you receive another ace when splitting aces?

Q 44—3 pts. On what blackjack hand(s) should you always double down?

A: 10 **B:** 11
C: 10 & 11 **D:** 9, 10, & 11

Bonus Q—2 pts. If you're betting ten dollars, can you double down for five dollars?

Double Bonus Q—4 pts. Is there ever a time when you should not double down on 10? If so, name the two dealer up-cards that should stop you from doubling.

A 43. *Never* split 4s, 5s, and 10s. Always treat

two 4s as 8 and hit it. Same goes for 5s. Treat that hand as 10 and follow basic strategy as to whether or not you double down or hit. Splitting 10s has got to be the dumbest move at a blackjack table. You have 20. Why take the risk of ruining a good hand? Most casinos today will not allow you to resplit aces. If you draw an ace on an ace, you have 12, and your only chance of winning that hand is a dealer bust.

A 44. *Always* double down on 11. It's a classic

rule of basic strategy that you must always follow. Yes, you can "double for less" but why? Basic strategy holds that you should not double on 10 if the dealer is showing a 10 or ace. Rare exceptions to doubling on 10, along with other strategy rules, are occasionally made by card-counters who would know, for example, that there is a dearth of 10-value cards and aces remaining to be played. Such exceptions, however, are not grounds for arguing an incorrect answer.

Q 45—5 pts. What are the odds of rolling a 7 at the dice table?

  A: 5 to 1   **B:** 6 to 5
  C: 6 to 1   **D:** 9 to 5

Bonus Q—3 pts. If odds are quoted as 4 to 1, does it mean there is a greater than even or lesser than even likelihood of a certain event happening?

Double Bonus Q—6 pts. What is 4 to 1 odds expressed as a percentage?

Q 46—5 pts. In the movie, *Indecent Proposal,* where were the casino interiors shot?

  A: The Sahara   **B:** The Desert Inn
  C: The Mirage   **D:** The Las Vegas Hilton

Bonus Q—3 pts. Name the three major stars of the movie.

Double Bonus Q—6 pts. Who wrote the novel on which the movie was based?

A 45. There are six ways to roll a 7 out of 36 total ways. That's 30 to 6, which is 5 to 1. The first number in an odds expression is the number of times an event should not happen. The second number is the number of times it should. So if there's a 4 to 1 chance it's going to rain tomorrow, it probably won't. Odds of 4 to 1 means there's a 20 percent chance of rain. One chance out of five is 1/5, yet another way to express probabilities.

A 46. If you were at the Las Vegas Hilton during 1992, you might have watched the filming for the blockbuster 1993 movie starring Robert Redford, Demi Moore, and Woody Harrelson. Jack Engelhard wrote the novel.

TIDBIT—Slot machine denominations range from penny slots to $500 tokens. Do you think anyone plays five tokens at a time?

Q 47—5 pts.

What was the fourth hotel/casino to open on the Strip? Hint: It would be the last major hotel to open during the '40s, joining the El Rancho Vegas, The Last Frontier, and The Flamingo.

A: The Desert Inn   **B:** The Sahara
C: The Riviera   **D:** The Thunderbird

Bonus Q—3 pts. To set this new hotel apart from the others, what new idea for entertainment did the owners try?

Double Bonus Q—6 pts. This famous hotel was christened with what new name in 1977?

Q 48—3 pts.

Name the nineteenth-century invention that would create a classic case of "oneupmanship" as the hotels flashed their names up and down the new Strip. Hint: It's still a big part of the Las Vegas scene today. Did you bring your camera?

A: Showgirls   **B:** Movie stars
C: Neon   **D:** High-rise hotels

Bonus Q—2 pts. By now, this stretch of the Los Angeles Highway became known as the Strip. What famous street in Los Angeles was the inspiration for the name? Hint: It was the name of a TV show in the '60s.

Double Bonus Q—4 pts. What major hotels opened in downtown Las Vegas during this decade? Name two.

A 47. The 1948 opening of the Thunderbird Hotel received perhaps more worldwide publicity than the Flamingo opening, even with its gangster connections, only two years earlier. Billed as the "Broadway Of The West," top theatrical shows were brought in, appealing to the more "sophisticated" crowds. By 1977, the competition was keen, and the Thunderbird became the Silverbird, signaling a steady decline in profitability.

A 48. It was as if all the new hotel owners had to have the biggest, tallest, brightest, most colorful sign. And neon was the answer. A downtown casino owner, who also happened to be a former Los Angeles police officer no less, coined the term *Strip* because the glitzy signs reminded him of Sunset Blvd. But the award for the most glitz had to go to the new hotels sprouting up in downtown Las Vegas. "Glitter Gulch" welcomed the Pioneer Club, the Golden Nugget, the Eldorado, Nevada Biltmore, and the El Cortez, joining long-established "clubs" and hotels such as the Boulder Club and the Apache Hotel.

Q 49—5 pts. The decade of the '40s also saw the first Las Vegas performance of what famous comedy team? Hint: The team would eventually split, but both entertainers would go on to successful solo careers.

A: Martin & Lewis   **B:** Ernest & Julio
C: Abbott & Costello   **D:** Burns & Allen

Bonus Q—3 pts. What hotel booked this great act? Hint: It also wooed Lena Horne, Bill "Bojangles" Robinson, and Jimmy Durante.

Double Bonus Q—6 pts. Name the small club that opened in 1947 on the Strip across from the El Rancho Vegas? It had a short history; collectibles from this club are rare.

Q 50—3 pts. What downtown hotel was home to "Vegas Vic" for more than 50 years?

A: The Pioneer Club   **B:** Union Plaza
C: The Mint   **D:** The Golden Nugget

Bonus Q—2 pts. What did Vegas Vic say?

Double Bonus Q—4 pts. How did this cowboy icon come to be?

A 49. The '40s set the trend for great entertainment. Las Vegas would never look back. Dean Martin and Jerry Lewis loved playing the Flamingo. Jimmy Durante, incidentally, was the Flamingo's opening headliner. Down the Strip, a new club with a small casino would open, but how could it possibly compete? It didn't. The Club Bingo became part of the Sahara Hotel in 1952.

A 50. The Pioneer Club had a long and storied history, but its real claim to fame happened in 1947 when the "Howdy Partner" cowboy was installed atop the club as a promotion sponsored by the Chamber of Commerce. It became a key part of downtown's marketing campaign and was even featured on the official Las Vegas logo of the time.

TIDBIT—The world's largest slot machine can be found at the Four Queens; six people can play it simultaneously.

Q 51—5 pts. As the decade of the '40s ended, another "marketing idea" was born in the "great scheme of things" that would help make Vegas what it is today. So what was it that "first" happened in 1949? Hint: It was a good thing McCarran Airport was growing and that airlines such as United were bringing in DC-3s full of visitors.

A: Card-counting publicized   **B:** A rodeo
C: A convention   **D:** Junkets started

Bonus Q—3 pts. The population of Las Vegas at the start of the decade was only a little over 8,000. What was the population by the end of the decade?

Double Bonus Q—6 pts. What nearby town was founded during the '40s, primarily to support growth in the chemical-producing industry southwest of Las Vegas?

Q 52—3 pts. What is the most common ploy today to cheat a slot machine?

A: Stringing   **B:** Magnets
C: Slugs   **D:** Infrared

Bonus Q—2 pts. If you hit a big jackpot on a mal-functioning slot machine, what's the most likely scenario?

Double Bonus Q—4 pts. If you get caught trying to rig a slot machine, what's the most likely scenario?

A 51. Dazzling signs, plush resorts, top entertainment, casino gambling, great weather. What more could conventioneers ask for? Las Vegas boasted of 25,000 inhabitants by 1949, but the big rush was yet to come. Meanwhile, surveyors were busy plotting out Henderson, Nevada, a nice "suburb" to live in, not far from Boulder City.

A 52. Although many high-tech means of tripping up the computers inside slot machines do exist, the most common "technique" is still "slugging." Casinos find literally tons of slugs every year when they empty machines. It's just another reason why many casinos are going to coin-less slots. If your machine is malfunctioning, don't play it. Why? Because if you win a jackpot, you won't get paid! The casino has a neat little gadget that can tell if a machine has been malfunctioning, *and* it can also tell if it has been tampered with. Casino operators make no bones about it: If you get caught trying to cheat, you'll end up in the pokey.

Q 53—3 pts. What casino table-game draws the largest bets?

   A: Craps   **B:** Baccarat
   C: Blackjack   **D:** Roulette

Bonus Q—2 pts. If we look at all the gambling options in most Las Vegas casinos today, what other form of gambling holds the record for the largest bet ever made?

Double Bonus Q—4 pts. What game draws the smallest wagers on average, and, in fact, is the most expensive for the casino to operate?

Q 54—3 pts. If 21 is the magic number at the blackjack tables, what's the number to shoot for at baccarat?

   A: 20   **B:** 19
   C: 8   **D:** 9

Bonus Q—2 pts. What skill is involved in baccarat?

Double Bonus Q—4 pts. What are the names of the two baccarat hands on which players bet?

A 53. Hands down, the biggest bets at the tables are in the baccarat pit. The casino generally sets aside a secluded area for this formal game, but anyone can walk in and play. Don't be alarmed, however, if the player beside you is betting $50,000 at a crack! The largest wager of all was made in a casino's sports book: two million dollars, and it wasn't even on the Super Bowl! The casino's "cheap" game is keno, and it's so labor-intense that little overall "net profit" comes from the keno parlor.

A 54. Either an 8 or 9 is called a "natural," and it usually wins. But 9 always wins over 8. There is no skill whatsoever involved in this game. It's basically a coin-flip, with players betting on either of two hands, called the "player hand" and the "banker hand." Answers of "player" and "banker" or simply "bank" or "bank hand" are also acceptable.

TIDBIT—Siegfried & Roy recently signed an entertainment contract with the Mirage for nearly $58 million, the largest on record.

Q 55—3 pts. What are the names for the two different ways to bet 12 numbers at a roulette table?

A: Street/double street   **B:** Column/dozen
C: Line/corner   **D:** Corner/column

Bonus Q—2 pts. What is the odds payoff if you win a "split" bet, and how do you make this bet?

Double Bonus Q—4 pts. What happens if a roulette dealer puts the marker on a "winning" number (on which you have a bet) and then realizes a mistake and replaces the marker on a different number?

Q 56—5 pts. What is the casino percentage when you make a football wager against the point-spread?

A: 10 percent   **B:** 5 percent
C: 4.5 percent   **D:** 5.5 percent

Bonus Q—3 pts. What is a "futures" bet?

Double Bonus Q—6 pts. What's the difference between a "money-line" and a "point-spread"?

A 55. Either the column bet or the dozen bet is an "outside" wager covering 12 numbers. You have a 1 in 3 chance of winning (so you're paid at 2 to 1), but we can't forget those green numbers that give the casino the edge. A split bet pays 17 to 1 and is made by placing your chip(s) centered on the line that separates two adjacent numbers. Surprisingly, most all casinos today will not pay on a number that was deemed a winner but then determined to be read by the dealer in error. It happens more often than you think.

A 56. You must wager 11 to win 10 when betting the point-spread. So, if you bet $11 on both teams, you will win $10 and lose $11. That's a $1 loss over $22 risked. It's an easy one to prove: 1/22 is 4.5 percent. A futures bet is offered at the beginning of a sports season, with certain odds posted for a team to go all the way: win the World Series, the Super Bowl, whatever the sport. A point-spread is a handicap assigned to the weaker team to try to make the contest relatively even for wagering. A money-line takes any weakness into account as part of the payoff. For example, instead of getting some points, a big under-dog might get you 2 to 1 odds.

Q 57—5 pts.

What wager at the craps tables is the worst percentage bet you can make?

A: Any 7   B: Place-bet
C: Field bet   D: Hardway

Bonus Q—3 pts. If a 6 or 8 is easier to make than a 4 or 10, then why do the 6 or 8 hardways pay more than the 4 or 10 hardways?

Double Bonus Q—6 pts. What is the percentage cost for making hardways?

Q 58—3 pts.

Blackjack has a unique set of player rules that tells you exactly what to do with every conceivable hand total and dealer up-card combination. What is the name of this set of rules?

A: Basic strategy   B: Card-counting
C: Optimum strategy   D: Player strategy

Bonus Q—2 pts. What are the four options a blackjack player has?

Double Bonus Q—4 pts. What is the key player-disadvantage in the game rules of blackjack?

A 57. The worst bet you can make is "any 7." It pays 4 to 1, but it *should* pay 5 to 1! As a percentage, that's nearly 17 percent against you! Since hardways lose when the numbers are made "easy," it only makes sense that the easier it is to lose it, the more it should pay. Hardways are expensive, but loads of fun! The 6 or 8 hardways cost a little over 9 percent. The 4 or 10 hardways will set you back a little over 11 percent.

A 58. The complete set of correct player options is called "basic strategy." There is never a need to ponder. You will either hit, stand, double down, or split. The big disadvantage to this game for you and me is the simple fact that we have to draw first. It's worth nearly 7 percent to the casino, but playing correct basic strategy, in addition to the extra payoff for a player's blackjack, cuts this percentage down to a nearly even game. But the casino still has a slight edge.

TIDBIT—$13 million was spent on the Las Vegas Strip in 1996 to improve traffic flow and beautify the boulevard.

Q 59—3 pts. If you are dealt an untied blackjack, at what odds is it paid?

A: 3 to 2   **B:** 2 to 1
C: 3 to 1   **D:** Even money

Bonus Q—2 pts. Under what circumstances should you take "insurance"?

Double Bonus Q—4 pts. Is a particular seat at a blackjack table better than others?

Q 60—3 pts. Which of the following blackjack hands is a "stiff"?

A: 8-8   **B:** 10-6
C: ACE-4   **D:** 5-6

Bonus Q—2 pts. Why do most casinos no longer allow a blackjack dealer to "peek" at the hole card when an ace or 10-value card is up?

Double Bonus Q—4 pts. Why do most casinos deal blackjack with the player's cards face-up?

TIDBIT—The average Las Vegas casino manager earns $150,000 per year, which probably works out to about $8 per hour.

A 59. Blackjacks are paid off at 3 to 2 odds. Bet $10 and win $15! Insuring a blackjack, the only time it would seem to make any sense at all, is still not a smart move. Over the long term, the cost of insurance outweighs the apparent advantage. If you are a beginner, it might be best to position yourself at the far left of the table, called "3rd base," so that you will have more time to study your hand and be ready when it's your turn.

A 60. A stiff is any hand that can bust (exceed 21) with a draw. Only 10-6 is a stiff because a 6 or higher draw will bust the hand. A hand of 8-8 should be split, not hit. Dealers are not allowed to look at the hole card to prevent them from signaling the card value to a confederate player. Cards are now dealt face-up so that players never need to touch the cards. Although some casinos may still deal cards face-down at a single- or double-deck game, the overwhelming concern is that an unscrupulous player might mark the cards.

TIDBIT—In Las Vegas, you only have a one in 35 chance that it will rain on any given day.

Q 61—3 pts. What is the average temperature in Las Vegas?

A: 95.2 degrees   **B:** 74.8 degrees
C: 66.3 degrees   **D:** 50.7 degrees

Bonus Q—2 pts. To the nearest inch, what is the annual rainfall in Las Vegas?

Double Bonus Q—4 pts. Although tornadoes and hurricanes are not a problem in Las Vegas, what type of "severe" storms are not uncommon?

Q 62—3 pts. What is the average humidity in Las Vegas?

A: 10 percent   **B:** 29 percent
C: 40 percent   **D:** 55 percent

Bonus Q—2 pts. Name any one of several advantages to living in a "dry" climate.

Double Bonus Q—4 pts. Does Las Vegas ever experience measurable snowfall?

TIDBIT—Las Vegas casinos win over $7 billion each year, nearly 80 percent of the entire state's gaming revenue.

A 61. It only seems like it should be 95.2 degrees, especially if you visit Las Vegas in the summer, when temperatures can exceed 110 degrees for days on end. Thanks to its relatively cool winters, the average temperature in Las Vegas is a comfortable 66.3 degrees. The northern climate of Nevada gets the most rain. Las Vegas would seem to have been "shorted," since only 4.13 inches fall yearly. Las Vegas is known for its spectacular electrical storms. Lightning displays can be almost otherworldly. Rather fitting, I would say, for the "Entertainment Capital Of The World"! Incidentally, "windstorms" or "sandstorms" is also an acceptable answer.

A 62. Most visitors would guess 10 percent, but it's actually 29 percent, which is still considered quite low. People with allergies or skin problems usually prefer a dry climate. And, best of all, Las Vegas does not have bugs! That's right. Not even pesky mosquitoes, thanks to the dry air and infrequent rain. There simply are no stagnant ponds for the little buggers to breed. Las Vegas does indeed see an inch or more of snow in some winters, but I doubt if any local residents own snow shovels.

Q 63—3 pts. Clark County, which includes Las Vegas, is home to what percentage of Nevada's total population?

A: 70 percent   B: 60 percent
C: 50 percent   D: 40 percent

Bonus Q—2 pts. How many people visit Las Vegas annually?

Double Bonus Q—4 pts. What is Nevada's most important industry?

Q 64—3 pts. What weekend in Las Vegas has the most weddings?

A: Memorial Day   B: Halloween
C: Valentine's Day   D: Labor Day

Bonus Q—2 pts. Why are weddings so popular in Las Vegas?

Double Bonus Q—4 pts. What are the requirements in order to get married in Las Vegas?

TIDBIT—Treasure Island is designed around the village created by Robert Louis Stevenson in his famed novel.

A 63. Although Reno might be Las Vegas' "older sister," it certainly doesn't have the "star appeal," which suits Reno and the rest of Northern Nevada just fine. If you want to party down, go to Vegas; if you want to pull off the boots and relax a spell, head for Reno. Indeed, Clark County is one of the United States' fastest growing metropolitan areas with over 70 percent of the state's population. Add to that, nearly 34 million visitors a year, and you have... uh... a traffic jam. But the idea is to keep 'em coming, because tourism is the state's key industry.

A 64. Boy, the questions don't get any easier than this one! It's not unusual for 3,000 weddings to take place over the Valentine's Day weekend. Weddings are popular because there's no blood-test requirement and no waiting period to think it over. It would be wise to do this when you're sober. All you need is some form of identification, a few bucks for the marriage license, a place to tie the knot, and... oh, yeah... a minister.

TIDBIT—High-roller suites at the MGM Grand are 6,000 square feet, complete with a private butler and chef to prepare your food.

Q 65—3 pts. What tourist attraction near Las Vegas features petroglyphs and artifacts of ancient Indian civilizations?

A: Lake Mead   **B:** Red Rock Canyon
C: Bonnie Springs   **D:** Valley Of Fire

Bonus Q—2 pts. Air tours of what distant tourist attraction draw Las Vegas visitors by the thousands each year? Hint: Experienced hikers would prefer a mule ride from the top to the bottom.

Double Bonus Q—4 pts. Yes, there's boating and fishing and even scuba-diving at what nearby recreation area?

Q 66—3 pts. What nearby mountain, at 12,000 feet elevation, features winter skiing?

A: Mount Baldy   **B:** Mount Rainier
C: Mount Everest   **D:** Mount Charleston

Bonus Q—2 pts. If it's 90 degrees in the Las Vegas Valley, what temperature is it at the top of this scenic mountain?

Double Bonus Q—4 pts. What does "Nevada" mean in Spanish?

A 65. Valley Of Fire State Park is a must-see only an hour's drive from Las Vegas. A four-hour drive gets you to the Grand Canyon. The air tours are great, but the mule rides are exhilarating. Pick a mule with good eye-sight because the ledges they walk on around the mile-deep canyon are only a few feet wide. Lake Mead is no more than 40 minutes from the Strip, the place to be on a hot July day.

A 66. If the heat's getting to you, other than the heat of a hot dice table, that is... just head for Mount Charleston, a good 30 degrees cooler than on the valley floor. (Answers of 60 to 70 degrees are acceptable.) What does "Nevada" mean in Spanish? It's an appropriate bonus question. "Nevada" means "Snowcapped."

TIDBIT—If you're a chocolate lover, visit Ethel M's in Las Vegas. The Mars family (you know, Mars Bars?) owns this one, too.

Q 67—5 pts. What is the name of the bay where a pirate ship battles with a British frigate in front of Treasure Island?

A: Tampa Bay   B: Buccaneer Bay
C: Bluebeard Bay   D: Barnacle Bay

Bonus Q—3 pts. Who wins the battle?

Double Bonus Q—6 pts. What happens to the ship that loses?

Q 68—5 pts. Where was the first Hard Rock Cafe built?

A: New York   B: Los Angeles
C: London   D: Las Vegas

Bonus Q—3 pts. In Las Vegas, the "Hard Rock" is known for doing what to "save the planet"?

Double Bonus Q—6 pts. Among its rare collection of rock 'n' roll memorabilia, arguably the hottest item is a jewel-encrusted piano that belonged to whom?

TIDBIT—Las Vegas counts over 152,000 slot machines; nearly 5,000 table games.

A 67. One of the Strip's top attractions for passersby, Treasure Island's Buccaneer Bay, draws crowds right off the street to watch a hearty exchange of cannon fire. The pirates always win, and the British ship goes down in 90 feet of churning water. Today, gambling in Las Vegas is all in the packaging. Hotel facades are attractions in and of themselves, but what's inside the package is all the same: If you see one casino... you've seen them all.

A 68. London was the scene of the first Hard Rock Cafe. With the addition of gaming, the Hard Rock Hotel & Casino in Las Vegas is unique in more ways than one. All glass, metal, and paper products used on site are recycled. The big "guitar" marquee is the draw on the outside, but inside, Elton John's flashy piano would put Liberace to shame.

TIDBIT—The average gambler in Las Vegas plays for about five hours per day. More than half of all gamblers play slot machines.

Q 69—5 pts. What Andrew Lloyd Webber musical played to record-setting performances at the Las Vegas Hilton?

  A: Cats   **B:** Phantom Of The Opera
  C: Jesus Christ Superstar   **D:** Starlight Express

Bonus Q—3 pts. What 1971 James Bond film featured scenes from this hotel's luxurious casino, not to mention a "high-wire act" atop the hotel?

Double Bonus Q—6 pts. What different name was given to the hotel in the movie?

Q 70—5 pts. What Las Vegas hotel is generally credited with having the first "theme park"?

  A: The Frontier   **B:** The MGM Grand
  C: The Mirage   **D:** New York-New York

Bonus Q—3 pts. This hotel changed its name in 1998, as recognition, some would say, of the end of what long battle that put a black mark on this legendary name?

Double Bonus Q—6 pts. Although the hotel seems to have undergone an identity crisis, what "icon" of this hotel hasn't changed?

A 69. Many of those who saw Starlight Express were so impressed by the musical score that the Hilton was besieged with requests for CDs, but none were available. Eventually, soundtracks from the London performance made it to the U.S. market. The soundtrack to *Diamonds Are Forever* was readily available and on the charts, thanks to Shirley Bassey's return to do the title song. The hotel was called "The White House" in the Sean Connery film.

A 70. Known as the Last Frontier when it opened in 1941, the Last Frontier Village was built next door, full of shops and "Old West" amusements. In 1998, the Frontier changed its name back to the New Frontier, as it was known from 1955 to 1967, following settlement of a long and bitter strike by the Culinary Union. Called in 1991, the strike was the longest in U.S. history. The New Frontier's sign is one of Las Vegas' most famous... and most photographed.

TIDBIT—The extravaganza simply known as "O" at the Bellagio cost over $100 million to produce.

Q 71—5 pts. Monet, Renoir, Picasso, and van Gogh are right at home in what lavish Las Vegas hotel?

A: The Venetian   **B:** New York-New York
C: Paris Las Vegas   **D:** The Bellagio

Bonus Q—3 pts. Billed as the most expensive hotel in the world when it opened in 1998, how much did this hotel cost to build?

Double Bonus Q—6 pts. To call it a "water show" is like calling the Kentucky Derby a horse race. What single letter of the alphabet names this hotel's dazzling attraction?

Q 72—5 pts. What Las Vegas hotel was of interest for purchasing by such notable celebrities as Wayne Newton and Johnny Carson?

A: The Aladdin   **B:** The Stardust
C: The Tropicana   **D:** The Desert Inn

Bonus Q—3 pts. What is this hotel's famous trademark? Hint: If you've stayed there, you know that even the faucets in the guest rooms bear this magical shape?

Double Bonus Q—6 pts. Perhaps the most famous wedding of all took place at this hotel on May 2, 1967. Can you name the couple?

A 71. The Gallery of Fine Arts in the Bellagio rivals top galleries around the world. Everything about this hotel is impressive, including its price tag of $1.7 billion. That's "billion" with a "B." And speaking of letters, "O" is the name of the spectacle that pianist Van Cliburn said was "like being in a Salvador Dali painting." A fitting comment for a hotel that is, in every way, a "masterpiece."

A 72. Johnny Carson never owned the Aladdin, but Wayne Newton did, in the early 1980s. From its chips to its faucets, Aladdin's magic lamp is everywhere. Of all the celebrities to be married in Las Vegas, the Aladdin scored the biggest coup in 1967 with the marriage of Elvis and Priscilla.

TIDBIT—Of the men who died building Hoover Dam, the first... and the last, were father and son.

Q 73—5 pts. What casino table-game has recently grown the fastest in popularity?

A: Blackjack   **B:** Roulette
C: Craps   **D:** Poker

Bonus Q—3 pts. What casino table-game has become rather flat in recent years?

Double Bonus Q—6 pts. What new casino game offers relatively low percentages compared to the old standbys?

Q 74—5 pts. Which of the following bets offers a player the best odds at a roulette wheel?

A: Red or black   **B:** Odd or even
C: A corner bet   **D:** A single number

Bonus Q—3 pts. What is the difference between a Single Zero and Double Zero roulette wheel?

Double Bonus Q—6 pts. What is meant by "clocking the wheel"?

A 73. Casino executives can't explain it, but craps is attracting more new players than all the other table games. As one casino executive said, "It's only taken a few hundred years for it to catch on." But it's always been popular in Atlantic City, where casinos typically have 4 to 5 times as many tables as in Vegas. Blackjack has flattened out in recent years, thanks mostly to countermeasures against card-counting. None of the new casino games—and there are many—offer attractive odds.

A 74. It's a trick question. All of the bets, except one, have the same percentage against you. Since the payoffs are the same for both a Single Zero and a Double Zero wheel, the 5.26 percent house advantage on a Single Zero and Double Zero wheel is cut to 2.7 percent on a Single Zero wheel (there is no Double Zero). Players who clock the wheel are looking for a relationship between where the ball is released and the segment of the wheel where the ball lands.

Q 75—5 pts. What is the house percentage in the keno parlor?

A: 5 percent   B: 10 percent
C: 25 percent   D: 50 percent

Bonus Q—3 pts. What is a "way" ticket?

Double Bonus Q—6 pts. What is the only "plus" to playing keno?

Q 76—5 pts. What hotel opened in 1950, becoming the fifth major resort on the Las Vegas Strip? Hint: Howard Hughes took up residence there in 1966.

A: The Desert Inn   B: The Dunes
C: The Sahara   D: The Tropicana

Bonus Q—3 pts. What "comedy team" opened the showroom? Hint: The guy who got all the laughs was wooden.

Double Bonus Q—6 pts. The Tournament Of Champions, held at this resort from 1953 to 1966, featured what game?

A 75. Most bets are 25 percent, but some are higher! A "way" ticket allows you to make multiple bets on one ticket. Circling 3 groups of 4 numbers, for example, means you are playing a 7-way ticket: 3 ways of 4 numbers, 3 ways of 8 numbers, and 1 way of 12 numbers. The only "plus" this game has is its high-odds payoffs. A few dollars can win thousands.

A 76. It took a while to build, but when the Desert Inn finally opened on April 24, 1950, everyone was talking about the hotel's rather bizarre color theme: Everything was decked out in Bermuda pink and emerald green, including the blackjack tables! Edgar Bergen and Charlie McCarthy opened the Painted Desert Showroom (pink and green, I imagine) along with Vivian Blaine. The "DI" had the first 18-hole golf course in Las Vegas, bringing such notables as Sam Snead and Gene Littler to its tournaments. That's right... the fairways were green, the flags were pink.

Q 77 —5 pts. Name the hotel that was known as "The Place In The Sun"? Hint: It opened in 1952; its "gingerbread" tower was completed in 1968.

A: The Sands **B:** The Showboat
C: The Sahara **D:** Sam's Town

Bonus Q—3 pts. The other Strip hotel that opened that same year had a catchy slogan, too. What hotel was billed as "The Jewel In The Desert"?

Double Bonus Q—6 pts. Which of these two hotels was imploded in 1996 to make way for what new mega-resort?

Q 78 —5 pts. What is the name of the first downtown casino to install carpet on the floor?

A: Golden Nugget **B:** The Mint
C: Four Queens **D:** The Horseshoe Club

Bonus Q—3 pts. What legendary casino owner bought this club in 1951?

Double Bonus Q—6 pts. What was the name of the club before he bought it and changed the name?

A 77. The Sands was "The Place In The Sun,"
while the Sahara became "The Jewel In The Desert."
Technically, the Sahara was a remodeled Club Bingo
that had sat across the street from the El Rancho
Vegas since 1947. The Sahara kept the 300-seat bingo
parlor. These two great hotels became the sixth and
seventh major resorts on the Las Vegas Strip. The
Sahara survives, but the Sands was demolished in
1996 to make way for the Venetian.

A 78. After the "colorful" gray-and-brown carpet
was laid, the Horseshoe Club had an unforeseen
problem: "We had to tell our customers not to squash
out their cigarettes on the floor," said Benny Binion,
who bought the Eldorado Club, a "sawdust joint" in
the old Apache Hotel. Soon after, Binion placed an
order for two thousand more ashtrays.

TIDBIT—As many as 5,000 people move to Las
Vegas each month. No one, apparently, counts
the number of people leaving.

Q 79—5 pts. What is the best bet you can make at a dice table?

A: Field bet   B: Pass-line bet
C: Odds bet   D: Come bet

Bonus Q—3 pts. How many come bets can you have working at any given time?

Double Bonus Q—6 pts. What does the term *handle* mean in casino parlance?

Q 80—5 pts. What is the standard color for a $25 chip?

A: Red   B: Green
C: Blue   D: Black

Bonus Q—3 pts. What is a chip "fill"?
Hint: Although it stops the game, it's certainly a positive sign for the players

Double Bonus Q—6 pts. What term does the casino use for "chips"?

A 79. The only fair bet in the casino is the "odds bet," which means the casino has no advantage on this unique wager. Since there are only 6 point-numbers on the dice table, a player could have five come-bets in the point boxes and one sitting in the come for a total of 6 come bets working. The "handle" is the casinos' term for all the wagers made by all the players. Not surprisingly, craps tables provide a big handle for casinos!

A 80. Although colors for $1 chips vary, all $25 chips are green. Such a nice color, especially when it's the color of all those chips stacked in front of you. If so, you've probably forced the casino to do a "chip fill" because the dealer's supply has been nearly exhausted. What a lovely fantasy. Soon, a security guard will escort a tray of more green "checks" to the table, the casino's term for chips.

TIDBIT—The Treasures Of Mandalay Bay is a museum full of rare gold coins and Nevada mining town memorabilia.

Q 81

—3 pts. If the casino thinks of you as a "whale," what are you?

A: Over-weight   **B:** A high roller
C: A cheater   **D:** A professional

Bonus Q—2 pts. If you "write a marker," what are you doing?

Double Bonus Q—4 pts. What happens if a credit player tries to stiff a casino?

Q 82

—3 pts. What does the casino's term *PC* stand for?

A: Per customer   **B:** Preferred customer
C: Percent   **D:** Private casino

Bonus Q—2 pts. What game does the casino consider its most vulnerable in the short term?

Double Bonus Q—4 pts. What does the casino rely on to make sure it always earns a profit over the *long* term?

A 81. Casinos just love "whales," the highest of the high rollers. These "premium" customers rarely play with cash; most play on credit by writing "markers," which are real checks that can be deposited against their checking account if they don't pay up. If a marker bounces, a collection agency will be put into action. Gambling debts, incidentally, are now legally enforceable in all states.

A 82. There is a cost for playing all casino games; call it a fee, if you like. Casinos call it the PC, which stands for "percent." Casinos earn their PC by paying off winning bets at something less than the true probability of winning those bets. The PC at the baccarat tables is relatively low, so casinos generally offer unusually high betting limits. But sometimes it can backfire and send a casino spinning in losses in the short term. But the law of averages, which is really the law of large numbers, always proves out over the long term, saving a casino from financial ruin.

Q 83—3 pts. "Comps" are a popular marketing tool for casinos. What does the term stand for?

A: Comparison **B:** Competition
C: Companion **D:** Complimentary

Bonus Q—2 pts. What casino game pays out more comps than any other?

Double Bonus Q—4 pts. What do players have to do to earn comps?

Q 84—3 pts. Casinos have rather degrading terms for players who make only modest wagers. Which of the following terms is *not* commonly used in reference to such a player?

A: Grind player **B:** Low roller
C: Nickel bettor **D:** Minnow

Bonus Q—2 pts. What other gambling endeavor draws more "small players" than any casino game?

Double Bonus Q—4 pts. At the start of any session of gambling, what should ideally be the size of your opening bet?

A 83. Most casino players like to play for comps, which means "complimentary." The more important question is, are they playing for comps or are they playing to win? Slot players get the most comps, but certainly not the biggest, which are usually reserved for high rollers at the table games. Slot players are rewarded with points on their slot-club cards, which can be redeemed for cash or gifts. What do you have to do to earn comps? Just play, of course. Play, and play, and play.

A 84. If a casino's biggest bettors are called "whales," are its smallest bettors called minnows? I would hope not. One of the chief reasons for the decline in the number of horse-racing tracks is average betting handle; it's actually less than a casino can earn from a nickel slot player. Who cares what a casino calls you if you like to begin play with table-minimum wagers? That's the smart way to bet! Increase your wagers *only* if you're winning.

Q 85—5 pts. What downtown Las Vegas hotel was the first to install an elevator?

 A: The Apache   **B:** The El Cortez
 C: The Mint   **D:** The Golden Nugget

Bonus Q—3 pts. What downtown casino was the first to receive a gaming license?

Double Bonus Q—6 pts. Name the oldest club on Fremont Street. Hint: Its name suggests that it belongs in a nearby city.

Q 86—5 pts. What was the first hotel/casino in Las Vegas? Hint: It's what "Las Vegas" means in Spanish.

 A: El Rancho Vegas   **B:** The Meadows
 C: The Nevada Hotel   **D:** The Pioneer Club

Bonus Q—3 pts. What downtown club was the first to banner its name in neon?

Double Bonus Q—6 pts. What downtown hotel would carry its famous name, decades later, to both Atlantic City and Laughlin, Nevada?

A 85. A tough series of questions. If you can answer all three, *you* should be writing this book. The Apache Hotel opened in 1932 with a new contraption: an elevator. Gosh knows it needed it; the hotel was all of 3 stories. Nearby, the Northern Club was already operating a casino, the first to be licensed in Las Vegas. But the Boulder Club, the oldest on Fremont Street, was already offering a game or two when it opened in 1929, two years before legalized gambling. It got square with the State in 1931, receiving the second gaming license issued in the county.

A 86. Although the El Rancho Vegas was the first hotel/casino on the Las Vegas Strip, and the Northern Club was the first "official" casino downtown, the Meadows, located on Boulder Highway, gets the nod as the first hotel/casino in Las Vegas. The first casino to install a large neon sign was the Boulder Club in 1934. Twelve years later, it would watch as the Golden Nugget opened across the street in 1946, a name that would defy time and distance with both Laughlin and Atlantic City casinos bearing the name.

Q 87—5 pts. What Las Vegas entrepreneur bought control of the Golden Nugget in 1972, turning the club into a major hotel/casino with the addition of two hotel towers?

A: Guy MacAfee   B: Steve Wynn
C: Donald Trump   D: Benny Binion

Bonus Q—3 pts. Eight years later, he would oversee the building of the Golden Nugget in Atlantic City in 1980. What is the name of this hotel today?

Double Bonus Q—6 pts. Another eight years later, he would build the Golden Nugget in Laughlin, Nevada. Name the major Strip hotel that would open only a year later under the direction of this prolific casino owner.

Q 88—5 pts. When a player is given the dice to shoot, what numbers win on the very next roll?

A: 7 & 12   B: 2, 3 & 12
C: 11 & 12   D: 7 & 11

Bonus Q—3 pts. What numbers lose on the very next roll?

Double Bonus Q—6 pts. What numbers must be repeated before a 7 is rolled in order to win?

A 87. Beginning his gaming career in 1967 as part-owner of the Frontier Hotel, Steve Wynn built an empire that included what is now Bally's Grand in Atlantic City, the Mirage in Las Vegas in 1989, Treasure Island in 1993, the Bellagio in 1998, and Biloxi's Beau Rivage in 1999. Guy MacAfee, incidentally, was the original owner of the Golden Nugget in Las Vegas.

A 88. Craps is such a simply game to play, but that doesn't necessarily mean it's simple to explain. A 7 or 11 is an immediate winner. A 2, 3, or 12 is an immediate loser. Any of the remaining numbers—called point-numbers—must be rolled again before a 7 is rolled in order to win.

TIDBIT—When making long-distance calls from your guest room, always use a calling card to avoid excessive hotel phone charges.

Q 89 —5 pts. What are the odds of getting a blackjack?

A: 10 to 1   **B:** 20 to 1
C: 25 to 1   **D:** 30 to 1

Bonus Q—3 pts. What is the significance of a "black" jack in a two-card 21?

Double Bonus Q—6 pts. How does a blackjack player use the option called *surrender?*

Q 90 —3 pts. Name the type of slot machine that most knowledgeable players look for.

A: Video   **B:** Progressive
C: Ghost   **D:** 3-coin

Bonus Q—2 pts. What is a ghost machine?
Hint: There's nothing to be scared about. Many of the multi-million-dollar jackpot machines have ghosts.

Double Bonus Q—4 pts. What is the difference between 3-coin and 5-coin machines in terms of percentages?

A 89. In nice round numbers, the odds are about 20 to 1. It probably seems like it's less often, and if that's ever the case, move to a different table. Many years ago, a blackjack that included a jack of clubs or spades paid off at 10 to 1, but not today. It makes no difference how the cards are suited. "Surrender" allows you to give up your bet in exchange for losing only one-half of your wager. Holding a 15 against a dealer's ace, for example, would favor surrender. Unfortunately, it's an option that is rarely found in casinos today.

A 90. Smart slot players look for progressive machines with an ever-increasing jackpot total. The higher the jackpot, the more it cuts into the percentages against you. Ghost machines have blanks where symbols should be. Some players don't like them, but it has nothing to do with percentages. The number of coins you need to play to win the jackpot doesn't affect percentages, either. But if you play less than the max, you *are* increasing the percentages against you by taking the jackpot out of play.

Q 91—3 pts. What is the title of the person in charge of a casino?

A: Pit boss   **B:** Superintendent
C: Casino manager   **D:** President

Bonus Q—2 pts. What is the next highest position in a casino?

Double Bonus Q—4 pts. Why are the bosses on the floor called "pit bosses"?

Q 92—5 pts. If you're playing at a table with a "shill," whom are you playing with?

A: Cheater   **B:** Pretend player
C: High roller   **D:** Professional

Bonus Q—3 pts. What is the difference between a high roller and a professional?

Double Bonus Q—6 pts. At what two casino table-games would you most likely find a "professional"?

A 91. Although larger casino operations might have a vice-president of casino operations, the person responsible for day-to-day operations is the casino manager. Directly under the casino manager are three "shift bosses" who are each responsible for one of the three 8-hour shifts. Gaming tables are arranged in groups called "pits," and each pit has a person in charge called a pit boss, whether male or female. There was an effort underway years ago to use the term *pit person,* but it just sounded corny.

A 92. Casinos still employ shills to act as players, but they're not really playing. They are also known as "game-starters." Why? Because at certain games— craps and baccarat, for example—most players won't play if there are no other players at the table. A high roller is merely a big bettor, not necessarily a good player. You'll always find the best players at the poker tables; the blackjack tables are a distant second.

TIDBIT—If you hit a jackpot on an idle machine, it was not just waiting for someone to pull the handle to get it. Today, computers determine the timing.

Q 93—5 pts. In the casino's race book, which of the following odds is the highest?

A: 3 to 2   B: 9 to 5
C: 2 to 1   D: 5 to 2

Bonus Q—3 pts. If the horse you pick to win goes off at 4 to 5 odds, how much will you win if you bet $5 "on the nose"?

Double Bonus Q—6 pts. Do professional handicappers bet their picks to win, place, or show?

Q 94—5 pts. In the 1995 movie, *Casino,* who played the role of Nicky?

A: Robert De Niro   B: Nicolas Cage
C: Danny DeVito   D: Joe Pesci

Bonus Q—3 pts. Name this award-winning movie's famous producer?

Double Bonus Q—6 pts. *Casino* was part of a crime trilogy. Name the other two movies in the series.

A 93. Odds of 9 to 5 are a little less than 2 to 1, which is the same as 10 to 5. Odds of 5 to 2 are a little more than 2 to 1, which would be 4 to 2. Odds are confusing to most first-time bettors. Odds of 4 to 5 means that for every five dollars you bet, you win four dollars. The pros at the track always bet their picks to win! Place and show tickets won't even pay your gas home.

A 94. Only one actor could do justice to this role: Joe Pesci. The trilogy was the treat of Martin Scorsese, whose other related films were *Mean Streets* and *GoodFellas*.

TIDBIT—If you want to play a table-game but have never played before, look for a table with no other players... and a friendly-looking dealer to help you.

Q 95—3 pts. What is the name of the hotel that looks like a castle, surrounded by a moat and drawbridge?

A: Coin Castle **B:** Excalibur
C: King Arthur's **D:** Knights Bridge

Bonus Q—2 pts. The corporation that owns this hotel also owns several others. Name two. Hint: Three of the four Strip hotels under this corporation are located beside each other.

Double Bonus Q—4 pts. Name the hotel's famous showroom.

Q 96—3 pts. What Strip hotel features the largest bronze statue in the world? Hint: It's right at the front entrance; you can't miss it!

A: MGM Grand **B:** Venetian
C: Luxor **D:** Caesars Palace

Bonus Q—2 pts. What entertainer packed this hotel's 17,000-seat Grand Garden Area to celebrate the millennium on December 31, 1999?

Double Bonus Q—4 pts. Everything about this hotel is big, especially the casino. How many football fields would fit inside the gaming area?

A 95. The Excalibur is owned by the same company that owns the Luxor, Mandalay Bay, and Circus Circus on the Strip. The 900-seat showroom is called King Arthur's Arena.

A 96. One of the most famous trademarks, the MGM lion, a 100,000-pound bronze statue, welcomes guests to the MGM Grand hotel. The lion is 45 feet tall, sitting atop a 25-foot pedestal. The hotel, incidentally, is lit at night in an extraordinary blaze of color and technology. It was Barbra Streisand who helped Las Vegas welcome in the new millennium at the Grand Garden Area, home to major concerts and sporting events. It seems as if everything in Las Vegas today is measured in terms of football fields. The MGM Grand casino, the world's largest, can take four of them.

TIDBIT—Have your film developed before you leave for the airport. Professional photographers take no chances with metal-detecting equipment.

Q 97—3 pts. Downtown Las Vegas casinos got a much-needed "shot in the arm" in 1995 with what bold $70 million attraction?

A: Carnival   B: Canopy
C: Circus   D: Outdoor theater

Bonus Q—2 pts. What is the name of this attraction?

Double Bonus Q—4 pts. Name any five of downtown's ten casinos.

Q 98—3 pts. If you want an authentic Coney Island hot dog, what Las Vegas hotel is the most logical choice? Hint: The Statue Of Liberty is there, too.

A: New York-New York B: The Big Apple
C: Times Square   D: Manhattan

Bonus Q—2 pts. Of the 12 Manhattan skyscrapers featured in the one-third scale facade, which is the most recognizable?

Double Bonus Q—6 pts. What famous bridge is there, too? Hint: I can get you a good price on it.

A 97. Old-timers still call downtown Las Vegas "Glitter Gulch," but it's been promoted since 1995 as the Fremont Street Experience. It's a huge, 90-feet-high canopy covered in over two million lights all controlled by a computer that produces dazzling images. It also produces high-energy music in sync with the sights that can make the bones in your ears vibrate. If you want to see (and hear) the "new" downtown, bring your money, your walking shoes, and your ear-plugs. The downtown casinos are: Horseshoe Club, California Hotel, El Cortez, Fitzgerald's, Four Queens, Golden Gate, Golden Nugget, the Plaza, and Las Vegas Club.

A 98. Yes, it has sauerkraut and mustard, and you can get it from a sidewalk cart at New York-New York, the tallest hotel in Nevada at the time of its construction. You can't miss the Empire State Building towering over all the others at 529 feet... that's 47 stories! It even has a replica of the Brooklyn Bridge, and this is no slouch, either. It's 300 feet long! Rumor has it that cab drivers even become rude when they turn in to the hotel.

Q 99—5 pts. What Strip hotel wasn't sure of its name until late in its construction? Hint: It was going to be called Desert Palace.

A: Desert Inn   **B:** Caesars Palace
C: Riviera   **D:** Tropicana

Bonus Q—3 pts. Name the hotel's famous showroom, and the entertainer who opened it in 1966?

Double Bonus Q—6 pts. Although Jay Sarno built this lavish hotel, it was later sold to two brothers from Miami who had made a fortune selling what product?

Q 100—3 pts. What does the word *roulette* mean in French?

A: Red & black   **B:** Little wheel
C: Big wheel   **D:** To spin

Bonus Q—2 pts. What is the difference between the European wheel and the American wheel?

Double Bonus Q—4 pts. What is a betting "system"?

A 99. So many names were tossed around for this behemoth on the Strip that no one was really sure what to call it. Call it Caesars Palace, and call it palatial. Its showroom may very well have the most recognized name: Circus Maximus, opened by Andy Williams who didn't waste any time getting to his signature song, *Moon River*. Brothers Stuart and Clifford Perlman owned the hotel for many years, parlaying a string of hot dog stands into one of the world's most famous hotels.

A 100. The "little wheel" in Europe only has a single green zero, while the American wheel sports two green numbers, zero and double zero. Because the payoffs are the same for either wheel, the European version is a much better game, but it's rarely found in U.S. casinos. The roulette table is where most "system" players hang out. Bets are made according to a predetermined scale of varying amounts, based on either the previous winning numbers or previous bet sizes. Let me sum it up for you: Systems don't work. But it's fun trying.

Q 101—3 pts. What are the two most popular number of lines on a multiple-line slot machine?

A: 2 & 5   **B:** 2 & 3
C: 3 & 5   **D:** 3 & 4

Bonus Q—2 pts. What is the difference between a single pay-line and multiple pay-line slot machine?

Double Bonus Q—4 pts. What is the difference between an "option buy" and standard pay-line slot machine?

Q 102—3 pts. Which of the following blackjack hands is "pat" (no draw) with a dealer's up-card of 10?

A: 2-K   **B:** 4-K
C: 6-Q   **D:** A-8

Bonus Q—2 pts. At the blackjack table, what is meant by a "soft" hand?

Double Bonus Q—4 pts. In casino parlance, what is a "push"? What is a less commonly used casino term that means the same thing?

A 101. One of the few things about slot machines that hasn't changed over the years is the multiple-line slot machine. On a 3-line machine, the 1st coin usually activates the center line, the 2nd coin activates the top line, and the 3rd coin activates the bottom line. On a 5-line machine, the 4th and 5th coins activate the diagonal lines. A single pay-line machine has only one line that's activated. Sometimes, by playing more coins, more symbols become activated. This feature is called "option-buy," and it can be found on multiple pay-lines, too.

A 102. A hand total of 19 is always a pat hand, so you stand. If you are dealt ace-8, you have a "soft" hand. Any hand with an ace has two values: counting the ace as either 1 or 11. So, the soft value is 19, the hard value is 9. Should the dealer turn over a 9 to go with her 10, she also has 19 and the game is a tie, which is commonly called a "push." Old-time casino bosses might still use the term *stand-off*.

Q 103

—3 pts. In the casino's race book, it helps to know the terminology. Here's an easy one: How long is a furlong?

A: 1/8 mile   **B:** 1/4 mile
C: 1/16 mile   **D:** 1/2 mile

Bonus Q—2 pts. What is meant by the term "odds on favorite"?

Double Bonus Q—4 pts. What is a "daily double"? Hint: You'll need to be sharp for the first two races.

Q 104

—5 pts. If a horse is a "standardbred," what kind of a horse is it?

A: Fillie   **B:** Broodmare
C: Stallion   **D:** Harness horse

Bonus Q—3 pts. What is the difference between a "pacer" and a "trotter"?

Double Bonus Q—6 pts. What is the difference between an "inquiry" and an "objection"?

A 103. A furlong is 1/8 of a mile, so a six-furlong race is 3/4 of a mile. If a horse leaves the post at odds of less than 1 (even money), it is said to be going off as the "odds on" favorite. The daily double is a bet that wins if you correctly pick the winners of the first two races. Some tracks also run a late daily double.

A 104. Standardbred horses are bred for the harness tracks. And there are two types, depending on their gait: A "pacer" paces by moving both the front and rear leg of one side simultaneously. A "trotter" trots by moving a front leg and opposite rear leg simultaneously. Breeders like to say that a pacer is "laterally" gaited, and a trotter is "diagonally" gaited. An "inquiry" is called when one of the stewards (race officials) suspects that an infraction occurred during a race. An objection is called when one of the jockeys (drivers) suspects an infraction.

TIDBIT—The Las Vegas Hilton built a new $10 million sign in 1997. It was rebuilt a year later at a cost of $4 million. It replaced a $5 million sign that worked just fine.

Q 105—3 pts. At the blackjack table, what
should you say if you want to draw another card?

A: "I'm good."   B: "Hit me."
C: Nothing   D: "Card."

Bonus Q—2 pts. Which of the following rules printed
on a blackjack-table layout is better for you: "Dealer
must draw to 16 and stand on all 17s" or "Dealer
must hit soft 17"?

Double Bonus Q—4 pts. What is a "bust" hand?

Q 106—3 pts. Most blackjack tables have how
many spots for player's bets?

A: 5   B: 6
C: 7   D: 8

Bonus Q—2 pts. How many players can be squeezed
in at a dice table?

Double Bonus Q—4 pts. How many players can be
accommodated at a roulette table?

A 105. Virtually all casinos today will not accept verbal signals. If you want another card, motion with your hand in a "scooping" motion toward you. Or, simply point to the cards with your finger, close to but not touching them. If you are in a game where the cards are dealt face-down, simply scrape the cards toward you. If a dealer must hit soft 17, it's a significant disadvantage to you. A "bust" hand, by either you or the dealer, is one that totals more than 21 and therefore loses.

A 106. Although it seems a little tight sometimes, virtually all casinos today order their blackjack tables with seven spots. If you think it's tight at a blackjack table, hurry over to a hot dice table and try to get in. Most tables today are built for eight players at each end, for a total of 16 players. The number of roulette players who can play at the same table is limited to the number of different-color chips the casino offers. Players must use different colors to distinguish their bets among the others. Generally, six players is the limit.

Q 107—3 pts. What casino game offers the most tournament action?

A: Poker   **B:** Craps
C: Blackjack   **D:** Slots

Bonus Q—2 pts. In tournament action, what game is the best if *you're* the best?

Double Bonus Q—4 pts. What is the entry fee called in a poker tournament?

Q 108—5 pts. What Strip casino was featured in *Rain Man*, the 1988 movie?

A: Caesars Palace   **B:** Las Vegas Hilton
C: The Rio   **D:** Desert Inn

Bonus Q—3 pts. Name the two award-winning stars of the movie.

Double Bonus Q—6 pts. What game was featured in the movie, and how was it beaten?

A 107. There are more slot players among all the games, so there are more slot tournaments. Many more! But if you happen to be a very good poker player, tournament play can mean more money in your pocket. Blackjack tournaments are difficult to win, even for expert players, because of special tournament rules that tend to alleviate much of the skill factor. In most poker tournaments, there is a "buy-in," not unlike a regular poker game, but winnings are determined by your finish.

A 108. The place was Caesars Palace; blackjack was the game. Dustin Hoffman played an autistic savant who beat the game by counting the cards. Tom Cruise played the role of his younger brother.

TIDBIT—In 1967, a Nevada bill was passed allowing corporations to own casinos. An individual owning a casino today... lock, stock, and barrel, is rare.

Q 109—3 pts. Name the hotel that opened on Boulder highway in 1954, resembling a Mississippi riverboat complete with smokestacks and a paddlewheel.

A: The Showboat   B: Gold Strike
C: Jackpot Junction   D: Sam's Town

Bonus Q—2 pts. What was the original name of this hotel?

Double Bonus Q—4 pts. What sport has this hotel popularized. Hint: It made its "strike" in 1959 and it's been in the fast "lane" ever since.

Q 110—5 pts. The Strip got its first "high rise" in 1955. Can you name the hotel?

A: The Stardust   B: The Dunes
C: The Riviera   D: The Tropicana

Bonus Q—3 pts. How many stories tall was this new hotel?

Double Bonus Q—6 pts. What was the first "high rise" in downtown Las Vegas?

A 109. It opened as the Desert Showboat Motor Inn, believe it or not, but now it's just the Showboat, a popular stop for locals, not to mention professional bowlers, who compete every year in one of the P.B.A. tour's top tournaments. When it expanded its bowling alley in the late '70s, it was one of the country's largest facilities with over 100 lanes.

A 110. Liberace opened the Riviera Hotel in April of 1955, getting a then-unheard-of $50,000 a week! It was the ninth major resort on the bustling Strip, standing tall over all the others at a whopping nine stories! A year later, the new 15-story Fremont Hotel in downtown Las Vegas would become Nevada's tallest building.

TIDBIT—If you are a table-game player, you can usually avoid the long lines to the showroom by asking a pit boss to escort you to the VIP line.

Q 111

—5 pts. What hotel, built in 1955, featured a 30-foot tall sultan standing over the entrance to the casino? Hint: The Bellagio is there now, sans sultan.

A: The Sahara   **B:** The Aladdin
C: The Desert Inn   **D:** The Dunes

Bonus Q—3 pts. At the far south end of the Strip, another hotel would open just a year later, contributing to Las Vegas' first room glut. Can you name it? Hint: The Mandalay Bay resort is there now.

Double Bonus Q—6 pts. What new regulatory agency in Nevada prevented this hotel from opening its casino until a year later?

Q 112

—5 pts. What hotel opened in 1957 as "The Tiffany Of The Strip"? Hint: The hotel still stands at the corner of the Strip and a major street named after the hotel.

A: The Flamingo   **B:** The Tropicana
C: The MGM Grand   **D:** The Sands

Bonus Q—3 pts. What was the hotel's trademark attraction, which became a Las Vegas icon?

Double Bonus Q—6 pts. In 1985, it introduced a new tropical theme called "Island Of Las Vegas," including what gaming novelty in one of its giant pools?

A 111. The Dunes Hotel may be long gone, but its sultan is still there in spirit. 1956 was a tough year for Vegas, with the lowest room occupancy rate in its history. The Hacienda Hotel became the first stop on the Strip for travelers from Southern California, but not many stayed when they found out that the Gaming Control Board would not allow its casino to open until nearly a year later.

A 112. When it opened, the Tropicana Hotel became the most expensive resort built in Las Vegas. It cost over $15 million, and that didn't include the cost of a 60-foot-tall tulip-shaped fountain in front of the hotel, pegged at a cool hundred grand. Its 1985 remodeling included a five-acre water park that featured "swim-up" blackjack tables. That's right. Swimsuits were the proper attire.

TIDBIT—Most pit bosses are happy to write out a "coffee-shop" comp for players who have been under their watch for as little as an hour or two.

Q 113—5 pts. Built by one of Las Vegas' most renowned gamblers, this 1,000-room hotel would feature the most photographed sign on the Strip. When it opened in 1958, it was the world's largest gambling resort. Can you name it?

  A: The MGM Grand   **B:** Caesars Palace
  C: The Stardust   **D:** The Aladdin

Bonus Q—3 pts. What was the name of this colorful Las Vegas pioneer? Hint: He had owned several clubs in Vegas, and ran gambling ships dating back to the early '30s.

Double Bonus Q—6 pts. Sadly, he never lived to see his hotel open. How did he die?

Q 114—5 pts. What hotel opened in 1968, ending an eight-year drought in construction of major resorts on the Las Vegas Strip?

  A: The Aladdin   **B:** Caesars Palace
  C: MGM Grand   **D:** Las Vegas Hilton

Bonus Q—3 pts. The hotel was not all new construction however. What was the name of the original hotel from which this new resort was built?

Double Bonus Q—6 pts. In 1997 the hotel closed, only to reopen again in 2000. Thus, what dubious distinction does this hotel now have?

A 113. Tony Cornero was the force behind the Stardust Hotel. Started in 1954, it took four years to complete. He made his name by operating three gambling ships that sailed out of San Diego in the '30s and '40s. Incidentally, gambling chips from the S.S. Rex, S.S. Tango, and S.S. Lux are now highly collectible. Cornero died with his boots on, shooting craps at the Desert Inn in 1955.

A 114. Milton Prell opened the Aladdin Hotel from the remnants of the Tally Ho, which had survived on the Strip since 1963 without benefit of a casino! With its re-opening in 2000, the Aladdin became the first hotel to be closed, imploded, and re-opened without a change in name.

TIDBIT—Hotels always reserve a block of rooms for unexpected VIP guests. The best time to try to get a room when "there are no rooms available" is after 6 p.m.

Q 115—5 pts. Las Vegas casinos handle over $25 million per day in credit alone. What common source do casinos use to help ensure the creditworthiness of their customers?

A: Central Credit   **B:** Casino Credit
C: Credit Corporation   **D:** First National Credit

Bonus Q—3 pts. What is the minimum amount of credit that most casinos will extend?

Double Bonus Q—6 pts. What is a "call bet"?

Q 116—5 pts. What hotel has had the distinction of allowing a betting limit based on a player's opening wager?

A: Horseshoe   **B:** Caesars Palace
C: Golden Nugget   **D:** The Mint

Bonus Q—3 pts. Why does a casino set maximum betting limits?

Double Bonus Q—6 pts. What are you playing if you are using a "Martingale" system?

A 115. It didn't take long for casinos to realize
the importance of having a central agency handle
credit. Today, Central Credit has records of all credit
transactions of all customers at all casinos. It put a
stop to the practice of playing one casino against the
other. Generally, the minimum credit you can apply
for at the table-games is $1,000. Statistics show that
the lower the credit-line, the greater the likelihood of
losing it all, so be careful. Nevada casinos, unlike
many other venues, can accept a "call bet," which is
a form of credit in the sense that you can announce a
bet without having the money on the table.

A 116. Walk into Binion's Horseshoe with a
million bucks in a suitcase, and you can put it all on
the line, so they say, and if you win, you can do it
again, but you can't bet *two* million. Your first bet
sets the limit. All casinos set limits, although most are
in the range of two to four thousand dollars. Casinos
set maximum-bet limits to protect themselves from
players who use a system of simply doubling a losing
wager, and continuing to do so until the player
ultimately wins.

Q 117—3 pts. If you received an "RFB" comp from a casino, what did you get "free"?

A: Room service   **B:** Room & airfare
C: Meals & drinks   **D:** Room, meals, & drinks

Bonus Q—3 pts. If you are not a credit player, how can you play for comps?

Double Bonus Q—6 pts. What is "walking money"? Hint: It's not something you'd want to strive for.

Q 118—5 pts. In what part of a casino are the best-paying slot machines located?

A: Main entrance   **B:** End of aisles
C: Carousels   **D:** No specific area

Bonus Q—3 pts. What does the term "slot mix" mean?

Double Bonus Q—6 pts. How does a casino change a machine's percentage?

A 117. If your bets are $50 or more, on average, and you play for five hours a day, on average, you are probably entitled to free room, food, and beverages. It might not be a suite, and it might not be gourmet dining, but it's free. Sort of. If you don't play on credit but want to be rated for comps, you must deposit "front money" with the casino, or at least make sure that a floorperson monitors your play. "Walking money" is the cheapest comp of all. What is it? It's a few bucks to get you home.

A 118. Casinos today do not place higher-paying machines in certain high-traffic areas as most players believe. Floor layouts today purposely route customers past slot machines on their way to showrooms, restaurants, and other attractions. But the "mix" of machines is what's important. They are carefully mixed in terms of percentage, coin denomination, and design variety. It takes more than a "screwdriver" adjustment to change a machine's percentage. Complete circuit boards would need to be replaced, which is rarely done today.

Q 119—3 pts. What are the four main chip denominations?

A: $1-5-25-100   B: $1-5-10-100
C: $1-5-50-100   D: $1-5-20-100

Bonus Q—2 pts. Is a casino chip as good as cash? Hint: Don't take this to the bank.

Double Bonus Q—4 pts. Do old casino chips have any collectible value?

Q 120—5 pts. Name the entertainer who was generally regarded as the all-time favorite of high rollers?

A: Elvis Presley   B: Wayne Newton
C: Liberace   D: Frank Sinatra

Bonus Q—3 pts. At what hotel did Neil Diamond make his first Las Vegas appearance?

Double Bonus Q—6 pts. At what hotel did Johnny Carson make his Las Vegas debut?

A 119. The standard chip denominations are: $1, $5, $25, and $100. They are *not* as good as cash! And that's true even in the casino that issued them! If it is suspected that you are not the rightful owner of chips, you may be denied the right to cash them. More so, casinos routinely change the design of their chips, and set a cut-off date for acceptance of the old design. Old chips do indeed have collectible value.

A 120. Whether it was Caesars Palace, the Sands, or the Desert Inn, casino executives knew they had a winner when Frank Sinatra's name was on the marquee. Neil Diamond was at the Aladdin in 1976, his first Las Vegas appearance. Talk-show legend Johnny Carson was a showroom favorite of the Sahara, beginning in 1964.

TIDBIT—Fremont Street is named after explorer John C. Fremont, but did you know that Carson City is named after Fremont's trusty scout, Kit Carson?

Q 121—3 pts. At what casino game is a pad of paper and a pencil a no-no?

A: Baccarat   **B:** Craps

C: Blackjack   **D:** Roulette

Bonus Q—2 pts. Is card-counting considered cheating?

Double Bonus Q—4 pts. What are the chances of being cheated at a major Las Vegas casino?

Q 122—3 pts. How often does a blackjack dealer "bust"?

A: 1 in 4 hands   **B:** 1 in 3 hands

C: 1 in 5 hands   **D:** 1 in 6 hands

Bonus Q—2 pts. Is there anything a blackjack dealer can do to help you win?

Double Bonus Q—4 pts. Is there a problem if I'm playing at a table where I know the dealer?

A 121. You can keep track of the decisions at baccarat, roulette, and craps, but not at the blackjack tables, because the bosses might think you're counting played cards. If you're counting the cards in your head, you aren't cheating. Even so, the casino won't want your business. Your chances of being cheated by a Las Vegas casino are slim and none. A casino license is much too valuable to risk.

A 122. A blackjack dealer busts more often than you do, because you have an option on hitting, whereas a dealer must draw to 16. Figure that a little less than one hand in three is a bust. If a dealer isn't busting at that rate, change tables. Since dealers no longer peek at hole cards, they can't signal the card's value to a confederate player. But they could, technically, help you win by overpaying you. If you're playing with a dealer you know, the dealer must tell the pit boss that you know each other.

Q 123—3 pts. At what casino game do previous results affect future results?

A: Roulette   B: Craps
C: Blackjack   D: Keno

Bonus Q—2 pts. Why do most Las Vegas casinos use multiple-decks at the blackjack tables?

Double Bonus Q—4 pts. Why is the device that holds the decks called a "shoe"?

Q 124—5 pts. In the 1997 film, *Con Air,* what Las Vegas landmark was shown being imploded to help create part of the movie's special effects?

A: The Landmark   B: The Dunes
C: The Sands   D: The Hacienda

Bonus Q—3 pts. Who played "The Virus," the psycho leader of the escaped convicts?

Double Bonus Q—6 pts. What actor got top-billing in this "action" movie?

A 123. Blackjack has the distinction of being the only game where previous results (cards played) affect future results. For example, if five aces have been dealt from a double deck after only six hands played, the likelihood of a future blackjack has been greatly diminished. Multiple decks tend to thin out these fluctuations, making card-counting less effective. The "shoe" sort of looks like one; other than that, I'm stumped.

A 124. The producers of *Con Air* filmed the implosion of the Sands tower in 1996, and later edited the scene into the movie as part of a spectacular plane crash on the Las Vegas Strip. The ringleader of the escape was played by John Malkovich. The star of the film was Nicolas Cage.

TIDBIT—The Las Vegas Convention Center offers 2 million square feet of exhibit space; hotel convention space throughout the city provides nearly another million.

Q 125—3 pts. What famous-name casino opened on the Strip without a hotel? Hint: It's painted pink and white.

A: The Dunes   **B:** The Barbary Coast
C: Holiday Casino   **D:** Circus Circus

Bonus Q—2 pts. Four years later it got its hotel; Ten years later, it tried to repeat the feat in what other gambling mecca?

Double Bonus Q—4 pts. Surprisingly, this Strip landmark has earned national fame for one of its restaurants, rivaling its main attraction. Can you name the eatery?

Q 126—5 pts. What Las Vegas hotel got its name as the result of an international contest, drawing 183,000 entries?

A: The Luxor   **B:** The Excalibur
C: Monte Carlo   **D:** The Bellagio

Bonus Q—3 pts. What year did this hotel open, becoming the largest hotel in the world at the time?

Double Bonus Q—6 pts. What mystical item is the hotel named after? Hint: It was embedded in stone.

A 125. That's right. Circus Circus is a *real* circus with a carnival midway under the big top. There's one in Reno, too. But this property is not all games for the kids (not to mention adults). One of its restaurants, called "The Steak House," has beaten out Chicago, New York, and Kansas City's prime. Make mine medium.

A 126. The resort-to-be was officially dubbed "Excalibur" on September 28th, 1988, two years before its 1990 grand opening. The build-up to this event was a marketing person's dream. It all started with a contest to "Name The Castle," awarding $25,000 to the winner. The gist of the legend is that "Excalibur," a beautiful sword embedded in stone, was pulled out by a young nobleman named Arthur, earning him the throne of England.

TIDBIT—In 1955, baseball commissioner Ford Frick prohibited major league baseball players from staying in Las Vegas hotels.

Q 127—3 pts. Which of the following landmarks are not featured at New York-New York?

A: Ellis Island
C: Soldiers & Sailors Monument

B: Grand Central Station
D: Grant's tomb

Bonus Q—2 pts. New York-New York's skyline features 12 skyscrapers. Everyone knows the Empire State Building, but can you name 5 of the remaining 11?

Double Bonus Q—4 pts. The hotel's "upscale" shops all feature the elegant facades of what famous New York street? Hint: The name for this shopping extravaganza is also the name of an "upscale" Buick.

Q 128—3 pts. What is the name of the famous MGM Grand lion?

A: Leo
C: Golden

B: Metro
D: King

Bonus Q—2 pts. When the MGM Grand first opened, what attraction featured the Wizard Of Oz characters? Hint: It was a "gem."

Double Bonus Q—4 pts. MGM Grand Inc., owns many other casinos, including the one right across the street. Can you name it?

A 127. We all know who's buried in Grant's Tomb, but you'll have to go to the real New York to see it. The other replicated buildings are: the Century Building, the Seagram's Building, 55 Water Tower, the Lever House Soap Co., the Municipal Building, the AT&T Building, the Chrysler Building, the CBS Building, the New Yorker Hotel, Liberty Plaza, and the Ziggurat Building. The shops are located on Park Avenue.

A 128. I would have guessed "Leo," too. But no, the MGM publicist says, "Our big pussycat is named 'Metro.'" Emerald City is gone now, replaced by something called the "Entertainment Dome." And if you don't like New York-New York across the street, don't go to the MGM Grand to complain about it. MGM owns that one, too.

TIDBIT—A casino's surveillance cameras are not only looking for card-cheats on the player's side of the tables, but for fast-fingered dealers as well.

Q 129—3pts. The longest-running production
show in Las Vegas is at the Tropicana. Can you name
it? Hint: I'll bet you can-can.

   A: Minsky's Follies   **B:** Lido de Paris
   C: Paris Revue   **D:** Folies Bergere

Bonus Q—2 pts. Name the television-news personality
whose father imported the show directly from Paris.

Double Bonus Q—4 pts. What new concept in
entertainment did this show introduce?

Q 130—5 pts. If you mark a 10-spot keno ticket,
what are the odds of hitting all 10 numbers?

   A: 50,000 to 1   **B:** 83,000 to 1
   C: 1,000,000 to 1   **D:** 9,000,000 to 1

Bonus Q—3 pts. Why is a keno game called a
"race"?

Double Bonus Q—6 pts. What is the smartest number
of spots to mark on a keno ticket?

A 129. On December 11, 1999, an alumni cast-member reunion enjoyed a special 40th birthday performance of Folies Bergere. The Tropicana claims that it's not only the longest-running stage performance in Las Vegas, but in the U.S. as well. Entertainment Director Lou Walters, father of Barbara Walters, brought the show to Las Vegas. Although the Dunes was first with bare-breasted showgirls, the Tropicana was first with, uh... bare showgirls, and the first to perform a French Can Can. Either answer is acceptable.

A 130. Ouch! It's 9 million to 1! If you hit 10 out of 10—and I know of no one who has—the casinos will take a big slice out for themselves! You'll be lucky to win a hundred grand, depending on your bet. When keno was first introduced in Nevada casinos, it was challenged by the Gaming Control Board as a lottery, and lotteries are not legal in Nevada. So, casino operators banded together and said that it's not a lottery, it's a horse race. They even starting calling it "Racehorse Keno"! Surprisingly, the Control Board relented. There are no "good" bets at this game, but if I were to play it, I would only bet 4 spots to lower the odds and minimize the percentage.

Q 131—3 pts. What game "broke the bank at Monte Carlo"?

A: Faro

B: Roulette

C: Twenty-one

D: Chemin de fer

Bonus Q—2 pts. Is there such a thing as a "biased" wheel?

Double Bonus Q—4 pts. What counter-measure does a casino employ to prevent a player from winning at a biased wheel?

Q 132—3 pts. There is a best scenario for a double down at the blackjack tables. You have what hand total, and the dealer has what up-card?

A: 11/6

B: 10/6

C: 12/5

D: 11/5

Bonus Q—2 pts. What part of blackjack basic strategy is most often misused by amateur players?

Double Bonus Q—4 pts. Is it possible for an inexperienced blackjack player to actually play so badly that the percentages against other players worsen?

A 131. In the late-19th century, a man did indeed win 100,000 pounds ($500,000) at Monte Carlo by looking for biased roulette wheels. Everything was painstakingly calculated, including the effects of red paint on the wooden compartments, the size and tightness of the dividers, warpage and out-of-balance conditions of the wheels. Sure, there are biased wheels. No wheel could be symmetrically perfect. But it's not worth the effort today. Casinos routinely change their wheels; there's always two or three in storage.

A 132. If your hand is 11, and the dealer's up-card is 6, that's the most optimum time to double down. Soft hands, which occur a little more than 10 percent of the time, are frequently misplayed. When hands are misplayed, it has no predictable effect on other players' chances over the long term, but it can impact on a card-counter's expectation (an improper draw, for example, when a dealer's up-card is low and an out-of-proportion number of high cards remain).

Q 133—5 pts. What is the most likely long-term outcome of a casino-run poker game where all the players are of equal skill and knowledge?

  A: 1 winner   **B:** 2 winners
  C: All losers   **D:** All break even

Bonus Q—3 pts. What is a casino "rake"?

Double Bonus Q—6 pts. How can you tell a good poker player from a not-so-good player?

Q 134—3 pts. What is the only slot machine game that requires skill?

  A: Video Keno   **B:** Video Poker
  C: Red, White & Blue   **D:** Blazing 7s

Bonus Q—2 pts. How many of the five dealt cards on a video poker machine can be discarded to make a better hand?

Double Bonus Q—4 pts. When are these draw cards selected by the machine?

A 133. If all the players are of equal skill and knowledge, and they play long enough, the casino wins; all the players lose. Even though you're not playing against the casino per se, you are fighting the casino "rake," a percentage of all pots that the dealer pulls out for the house. Only if a player or two are not skilled can a good player win enough to outlast the rake. You can't pick out the good players; not at first, anyhow. Good players never give themselves away.

A 134. Video poker machines are indeed skill games. All reel-type machines, and video keno, are purely "luck of the draw." You may discard all five cards dealt if you like, and you'll get five new cards. These drawn cards, incidentally, were selected at the time the original hand was dealt. Behind each dealt card on the screen is a draw card ready to appear on command. Few players know this.

Q 135—3 pts. If a video poker machine deals you a hand of 3-4-5-2-6 of different suits, what do you have?

  A: Garbage   **B:** 4 to a straight
  C: Straight   **D:** 3 to a straight

Bonus Q—2 pts. Some video poker machines only return your bet on two pair, no different from holding only a high pair. If that's the case, what should you draw if you are holding two jacks and two 5s?

Double Bonus Q—4 pts. On a progressive video poker machine, how high does the jackpot have to go in order for the advantage to swing to the player?

Q 136—3 pts. What Las Vegas hotel features an erupting volcano every few minutes?

  A: The Mirage   **B:** Treasure Island
  C: Mandalay Bay   **D:** Luxor

Bonus Q—2 pts. Name the illusionists who perform regularly at this well-known hotel?

Double Bonus Q—4 pts. What is the name of the habitat where many of the illusionists' exotic animals are kept?

A 135. I remember this hand as if it were yesterday because I watched a gentleman get it on a $25 (that's *dollar*) poker machine. He invested $125, was dealt a straight, and threw it away! Straights can be the easiest to slip by. With two jacks and two 5s on a machine that only returns your bet on two pair, draw three, keeping the two jacks. Professional video-poker teams are looking for jackpots that are more than twice as high as the starting jackpot. On a quarter machine, for example, the royal flush jackpot must be at least $2,000.

A 136. That famous volcano has become the Mirage's signature attraction. And so are Siegfried & Roy, a must-see for all Vegas newcomers. Although the white tigers are kept in their own special habitat, most of the exotic animals—many are used in the show—are kept in the "Secret Garden."

TIDBIT—"Whiskey is the greatest gambling tonic in the world," said the Horseshoe's Benny Binion. Where other casinos offer a 3/4 shot, Binion's pours a shot and a half.

Q 137—5 pts. Name the 1995 movie about an alcoholic who went to Vegas to drink himself to death?

A: Fatal Attraction   **B:** Rounders
C: Leaving Las Vegas   **D:** Snake Eyes

Bonus Q—3 pts. Who played the role of the alcoholic?

Double Bonus Q—6 pts. Who played the hooker who loved him enough not to stop him?

Q 138—3 pts. What downtown hotel has the single largest nugget of gold in the world on display?

A: Horseshoe   **B:** Golden Nugget
C: Pioneer Club   **D:** Four Queens

Bonus Q—2 pts. What name has been given to this famous nugget?

Double Bonus Q—4 pts. How much does it weigh? Hint: It's bigger than a breadbox.

A 137. Hollywood could stand more happy endings. Nicolas Cage played the drunk in *Leaving Las Vegas;* Elisabeth Shue played the hooker.

A 138. Duh. The nugget is at the "Nugget," where else? And don't think you're going to walk right in and heist this thing. The "Hand Of Faith," as it's called, weighs 62 pounds; Your guess is as good as mine how much the armed guard weighs.

TIDBIT—A player's betting a hundred dollars right beside another player betting *two* dollars. So who's sweating the bet? The two-dollar player... if he's down to his last dollar.

Q 139—3 pts. Name the famous Strip hotel
where the "Rat Pack" hung out?

A: The Sahara   **B:** The Sands
C: The Riviera   **D:** The Tropicana

Bonus Q—2 pts. The Rat Pack included five top-name
entertainers. Can you name them?

Double Bonus Q—4 pts. What hotel stands today
where this '60s phenom made so many great
memories?

Q 140—5 pts. What small casino, known for its
sports-betting contests, was located at the present site
of the Mirage?

A: Castaways   **B:** Silver Slipper
C: Bonanza   **D:** Morocco

Bonus Q—3 pts. What other small casino was in the
way of a parking lot expansion at the Frontier Hotel?

Double Bonus Q—6 pts. Name the hotel that stood at
the southeast corner of Flamingo and the Strip, eyed
by Kirk Kerkorian in his bid to built the original
MGM Grand.

A 139. Great memories, indeed. No matter how pretentious, how big, or how expensive, the Venetian Hotel should know that it's sitting on sacred ground. The Sands Hotel defined an era in Las Vegas that I hope you were fortunate enough to witness. It was the place where Frank Sinatra, Sammy Davis, Jr., Peter Lawford, and Joey Bishop entertained in the Copa Room, and the lounge, no less, like Vegas will never know again.

A 140. When David meets Goliath in Las Vegas, the big guy always wins. So it goes for small casinos such as the Castaways, sitting square in the path of bulldozers clearing the way for the Mirage. The Silver Slipper, however, was traded in for a parking lot needed by the Frontier. And the Bonanza, a little 160-room hotel, had unknowingly been built beyond its own property lines, but after a court battle, Kerkorian got all the land he needed to erect his giant-sized MGM Grand (now Bally's).

Q 141—3 pts. It looked like a space ship, even a little bit like Seattle's Space Needle. Can you name this hotel that was ceremoniously imploded in 1995?

A: The Stratosphere   **B:** The Dunes
C: The Skyscraper   **D:** The Landmark

Bonus Q—2 pts. This hotel was closed long before the implosion. When did it open, and when did it officially close?

Double Bonus Q—4 pts. Who owned this strange-looking hotel?

Q 142—3 pts. When you think about "Mardi Gras" or "Carnivale," what hotel comes to mind?

A: Circus Circus   **B:** Mandalay Bay
C: Treasure Island   **D:** The Rio

Bonus Q—2 pts. Name the hotel's newest feature attraction, opened in 1997 at the same time its towering 41-story, 1,000-room addition was completed?

Double Bonus Q—4 pts. Name the hotel's version of Mardi Gras? Hint: If you have a mask, you can join in!

A 141. Howard Hughes bought the Landmark Hotel in 1968 while it was under construction. No doubt it had more "modern" appeal in those days, looking like something the Jetsons would fly around in, but it never really got off the ground. Hughes' wife, actress Jean Peters, took title to this "white elephant" as a result of her divorce settlement. Opened in 1969, it closed in 1991, and was destroyed in 1995.

A 142. It's always party-time at the Rio! Opened in 1990, this beautiful hotel brought a new look to Vegas, including its Masquerade Village, opened in 1997. The Rio's popular Masquerade Show treats guests to outlandish performances several times a day.

TIDBIT—Don't confuse baccarat with its dangerous European cousin, Chemin de Fer, where the player with the shoe does indeed take a risk by actually banking the bets of the other players.

Q 143—5 pts. Sam Boyd, a Las Vegas pioneer in the casino industry, built a hotel on Boulder Highway in 1979, after years of successfully running other hotels. Can you name it?

A: Sam's Town   **B:** The Showboat
C: Railroad Pass   **D:** Gold Strike

Bonus Q—3 pts. Name the Strip hotel, mired in trouble in the early '80s, that was taken over by Sam Boyd in 1985, restoring its reputation and returning it to prominence.

Double Bonus Q—6 pts. Sam Boyd opened a downtown hotel in 1971 on the site of the old Union Pacific Railroad station. Can you name it?

Q 144—3 pts. Name the Las Vegas hotel, generally credited with the largest national advertising campaign to promote its opening, which featured cranes shown lifting the Eiffel Tower onto its "new" foundation.

A: The Bellagio   **B:** Paris Las Vegas
C: Monte Carlo   **D:** Stratosphere

Bonus Q—2 pts. During the 1999 opening, visitors were treated to startling re-creations of what other famous French landmarks?

Double Bonus Q—4 pts. How tall is the "real" Eiffel Tower? How tall is the replica in Las Vegas?

A 143. Sam Boyd is a story of perseverance. Starting out as a dealer in the early '40s, he parlayed his savings into a piece of the Sahara, then joined Milton Prell—who had owned the Sahara—in building downtown's Mint in 1957. Next on his list was Union Plaza in 1971, sporting the world's largest casino at the time. He cleaned up the Stardust Hotel in 1985, and went on to build Sam's Town, one of Las Vegas' most popular hotels, particularly among the locals.

A 144. This $800 million resort's signature is most definitely the 50-story-tall replica of the Eiffel Tower. The original is 984 feet tall. Visitors can also enjoy the Arc de Triomphe, Champs Elysee, the Paris Opera House, Parc Monceau, and—believe it—the River Seine.

TIDBIT—Always put some of your winnings aside to ensure that you quit winners. Never, under any circumstances, press a losing wager.

Q 145

—3 pts. You can't miss its huge sign just off Interstate 15 on Sahara Avenue. Name this popular "locals" hotel?

A: The Sahara   **B:** Palace Station
C: The Showboat   **D:** The Gold Coast

Bonus Q—2 pts. Before its name was "upgraded" in 1983, what was this hotel called? Hint: B-8, O-11, G-13.

Double Bonus Q—4 pts. It's now part of a family of hotel/casinos, all bearing similar names. Can you name two?

Q 146

—5 pts. What Strip hotel features 3,646 rooms, but 424 of those rooms are operated by a different hotel?

A: Mandalay Bay   **B:** The Rio
C: Bally's   **D:** Monte Carlo

Bonus Q—3 pts. Describe the main hotel's signature attraction.

Double Bonus Q—6 pts. What year did this top-notch resort open?

A 145. Palace Station has one of the biggest signs in Las Vegas. It has to. It's not on the Strip; it's not downtown. It's not even on Boulder Highway. It's on Sahara Avenue, which means that famous sign has a big job to do in luring travelers off I-15. But the Palace Station draws plenty of local customers, going back to the days when it was the Bingo Palace. Some locals still call it that. This successful hotel is part of a corporation that owns Boulder Station, Texas Station, and Sunset Station.

A 146. Mandalay Bay is unique in the sense that it "shares" its property with the famous Four Seasons Hotel, Las Vegas' first Five Diamond award winner. For those staying at the Four Seasons, guests enjoy a private entrance, parking, and check-in. Mandalay Bay features a "wave pool," complete with white sand beaches and tropical plants. Built in 1999, this is truly the place to go if you want to be pampered.

Q 147—5 pts. In 1998, Hilton Hotels Corporation spun off its gaming division. What was the name of this new company?

A: Mirage Resorts, Inc.   **B:** Circus Circus Enterprises
C: MGM Grand Inc.   **D:** Park Place Entertainment

Bonus Q—3 pts. Name three other hotels, besides the Las Vegas Hilton, controlled by the same corporation.

Double Bonus Q—6 pts. Name two Atlantic City hotels under the same corporate umbrella.

Q 148—5 pts. Which of the following casino games is the least complicated to play?

A: Blackjack   **B:** Roulette
C: Poker   **D:** Craps

Bonus Q—3 pts. Which of these games is the most complicated?

Double Bonus Q—6 pts. Name the basic bet at a craps table, and describe it.

A 147. Hotel guests and gamblers might not have cared, but those who watched the stock market did. Park Place Entertainment owns the Las Vegas Hilton, the Flamingo Hilton, Bally's, and Paris Las Vegas. It also owns Park Place and Bally's Grand in Atlantic City. In 2000, a $3 billion deal added all of Caesars World holdings to this powerful group, including Caesars Palace on the Las Vegas Strip.

A 148. The table layout makes craps look complicated, but it's actually the easiest to play, assuming that you limit yourself to only the smart bets. Blackjack is the toughest game to master, but it's worth the effort if you want to develop a skill. The basic craps bet is simple: It's called a "pass-line" bet, and usually everyone at the table makes it. The problem is, players tend to make other bets that are not as good. A bet on the pass-line wins if a 7 or 11 is tossed. The bet loses if a 2, 3, or 12 rolls. If any of the other numbers roll: 4, 5, 6, 8, 9, or 10, that number must be repeated before a 7 is rolled in order to win.

Q 149—3 pts. What is the most coins one should ever play in a slot machine at one time?

A: 2 coins   **B:** 3 coins
C: 5 coins   **D:** The max

Bonus Q—2 pts. What are "celebrity" slot machines?

Double Bonus Q—4 pts. Some slot players only play machines with multi-million-dollar jackpots. What's wrong with this notion?

Q 150—5 pts. Most wise gamblers never play against percentages of three percent or more. Which of the following games does this eliminate?

A: Roulette   **B:** Craps
C: Slot Machines   **D:** Blackjack

Bonus Q—3 pts. Of all the new casino games, which game comes in under three percent?

Double Bonus Q—6 pts. What bet offers the lowest, constant percentage of all the games?

A 149. The answer is "the max" but it must be qualified. Virtually all machines today offer a bonus jackpot for "maximum coins in." Unless the maximum is more than 5 coins, always do it. But if a machine takes more than 5 coins, don't play it. A quarter machine that takes 20 coins is a dollar machine in disguise! "Celebrity" machines come and go in popularity, but they are all themed, in some way, to a famous singer, actor, whomever. With royalties and licensing rights to pay, I can only assume these costs are built into the percentages. Multi-million-dollar jackpots are hit, on average, by only one player out of six million. Do you really want to buck those odds?

A 150. At a little over five percent, roulette doesn't belong on the list. The lowest percentage bet is a pass-line bet or come bet at the dice tables with double or triple odds. None of the new games I've reviewed would make the list, either. Let It Ride, for example, is about four percent. Caribbean Stud Poker is a little over five percent.

CHAPTER 3

Fun Facts

Howard Hughes certainly left his mark on Las Vegas, and he left a few bucks when he died. His estate was contested for years, and several wills were presented to the courts, but all were declared bogus. Estimates on the value of his estate vary, but it is believed that nearly $7 billion was split up among two dozen *distant* relatives.

If someone were to ask you how much money Las Vegas casinos make every year from slot machines, you probably wouldn't know, would you? But you would admit, wouldn't you, that some of it is yours?! Here's a fact that's hard to believe: Almost 60 percent of all the casino profits comes from slot machines! Hmmm. Maybe we should be playing baccarat.

When you're at the Mirage, be sure to visit the 2.5 million-gallon Dolphin Habitat, the largest saltwater pool in the world. The Atlantic bottlenose dolphins that romp and play with each other are a treat to watch, but they cannot survive in fresh water. The Mirage is quick to point out that none of the dolphins were taken from the wild.

Las Vegas gamblers who play in other venues no doubt have visited an Indian casino in some part of the country. There are now literally hundreds, from the plush Foxwoods Casino in Ledyard, Connecticut, and the Soaring Eagle in Mt. Pleasant, Michigan, to the smaller upstarts in California. The major Indian casinos are often designed to resemble a rustic lodge, almost always decorated in Native American tradition, with Indian art and crafts galore. The feeling you get is as if you're walking through a museum, or a gallery of Indian lore. The effects are quite stunning.

But did you know that Las Vegas also had its own "Indian" casino, of sorts? That's right. The Thunderbird, the fourth hotel on the Las Vegas Strip, was built in 1948 and named to honor the Navajo legend of the Thunderbird as "The Sacred Bearer Of Happiness Unlimited." The hotel featured portraits of famous Native Americans, and included the most extensive collection of Indian art and beaded work imaginable. A turquoise-beaded thunderbird, valued at over $20,000, was enshrined at the hotel as if it were the Hope diamond.

The Thunderbird lost its "happiness" in the late '50s when accusations of mob infiltration virtually doomed this Las Vegas landmark. The hotel struggled until 1976, when it was sold and renamed the "Silver Bird." It was again sold in 1981 and renamed the "El Rancho." Of course, it had nothing to do with the original El Rancho Vegas, but it was hoped that, somehow, the name could restore it to prominence. It didn't. One of the founding fathers of the Las Vegas Strip is now just a memory.

When Las Vegas was just growing up, the most popular playground for Tinsel Town's rich and famous was Palm Springs, Calif. But Palm Springs had no casinos. Well, today it has casinos everywhere. If the Indians of that desert oasis had read the fine print in their treaties a little sooner, this book would be titled *Palm Springs Trivia*.

And speaking of Tinsel Town, the opening performance of "Hallelujah Hollywood" marked an otherwise slow 1974 in Las Vegas. The hottest tickets in town were ringside seats for this showgirl spectacular in the MGM Grand's Ziegfeld Room. With Dean Martin in the Celebrity Room, not to mention the world's largest casino (at the time) jammed to the hilt, this one-year-old behemoth on the Strip was THE place to be.

The El Rancho Vegas is said to have been the first Las Vegas hotel to offer buffets. The cost: one dollar. The Mint downtown claimed it was the first to offer that other Las Vegas tradition... the 50-cent shrimp cocktail. And the Union Plaza downtown said in its press release that it was "...the first to offer women dealers." So how many do you want?

As you might imagine, casinos have the most elaborate security systems in the world. Sensitive cameras can zoom in and read the date on a quarter, just before it's fed to a hungry slot machine. And those cameras are one of the reasons why your own personal cameras are not allowed in casinos. A flash can knock out the surveillance equipment.

But another important reason goes back to the glory days of Vegas when mobsters were frequent guests of hotels. For some reason, these guys just didn't like being in someone else's family photo album. "Hey, Ethyl, who's that guy standing behind you with that big scar on his face?" "Uh, I think that's Al Capone." "Wow!"

No one is exactly sure who actually discovered Las Vegas. No, it wasn't Bugsy Siegel. The valley that would become Las Vegas lay hidden for centuries, known only to Indians who settled there, protected from discovery by the harsh Mojave Desert.

Then, in 1829, a Mexican trader named Antonio Armijo, led a 60-man mule-team along the Spanish Trail, carrying loads of Boraxo to Los Angeles. They camped about 100 miles north of what is now Las Vegas. A young Mexican scout, Rafael Rivera, left camp one evening, upset that he had lost all his money in a crap game, and stumbled onto an artesian spring. This abundant source of water would change the route to Los Angeles, which became known as Interstate 15.

Seriously, as early as 1830, the name *Vegas* is actually shown on some maps. "Vegas" is Spanish for "meadows."

An attraction that many visitors are not aware of is ghost towns. Nevada is full of them, and there's at least three within driving distance of Las Vegas. You want to go see one? I don't know where they are, but ask a bellman. If you're bored with the games, or the convention you're supposed to be attending, and you want to go out in the desert by yourself, like an idiot, and get lost, that's your business.

Las Vegas has some really incredible rain storms that can drench the city in a matter of hours. Some of the worst floods have stacked up cars and literally moved buildings. When there's a flood warning, and you see water rushing into the casino, most sensible players get out. But not slot players, apparently. They just stay there playing in five inches of water! Someone has to remind these diehards that slot machines are electrical!

If you're heading for Hoover Dam, you'll probably pass through Boulder City, a quaint town with a most interesting point of trivia: Boulder City is the only town in Nevada where gambling is *not* legal!

Are gambling profits considered taxable income? Ask any slot player and the answer is, "Yeah, if it's $1,200 or more." Any payout of that amount or more, as any rookie slot player knows, gets tagged with a W2G, that infamous piece of paper, a copy of which goes to you, another copy to the casino, and the third copy to the dreaded IRS. That's right. They are expecting you to show the income on that year's tax return, so you had better do it. Of course, as any rookie CPA knows, you can also show gaming losses on that same year's return to offset all or part of your winnings. Incidentally, all gambling profits are considered taxable income, W2G or not.

Yeah, right.

Walk into any Las Vegas casino and plop ten thousand dollars in cash on the table, and guess what? There will be a little paperwork first, before you can have a little fun. Another federal statute, called Title 31, requires all casinos to report cash transactions of $10,000 or more. It's a bigger problem in the sports books where $10,000 bets are becoming routine. Now if it just so happens that you *won* $10,000, that's different. The Feds are only interested in catching "money launderers" who bring the cash in, not money *winners* who take the cash out. Of course, you still have to report your winnings on your tax return.

Yeah, right.

Jay Sarno built two of Las Vegas' most eye-catching hotels: Caesars Palace in 1966 and Circus-Circus in 1968. If you look closely at the cement lattice-work that completely encases Caesars Palace, through which that eerie blue-green light emanates, you'll see that the design is made up of cast-cement blocks in the shape of a square "S." So now we know that Sarno had at least a touch of ego.

Bally's Manufacturing Co., one of the two top slot machine manufacturers in the world, came to a stark realization in the late '70s. The Bally's board said "enough already" with making a lousy few bucks every time they shipped a machine out the door, just so all those greedy casinos could make thousands of dollars off *their* stuff.

So, in 1979, they built Bally's Park Place in Atlantic City and loaded it up with slot machines, only to find out Atlantic City has some goofy rule about a casino, owned by a slot machine manufacturer, installing its own machines. So, in 1986, they met Kirk Kerkorian, then owner of the MGM Grand in both Las Vegas and Reno, and made him an offer he couldn't refuse. Voilà! The MGM Grands became Bally's. Next, they tracked down Steve Wynn, then owner of the Golden Nugget in Atlantic City, and made *him* an offer he could refuse, but he didn't. The Golden Nugget became Bally's Grand.

But then Hilton came along in 1996 and bought up the Bally's this and Bally's that and now no one knows who owns what.

If only Hilton made slot machines.

A Las Vegas attraction you probably *don't* want to see is the underground testing of atomic bombs. The Nevada Test Site, about 65 miles northwest of Las Vegas, was the site of the first atomic bomb explosion in 1951. Until 1962, all the tests were done in the atmosphere. Kaboom! And you thought the Mirage's volcano was something! Las Vegas put a stop to these above-ground tests after Aunt Millie's meatloaf started to glow. Since then, all tests—and there have been over 500 of them—are done underground. Either way, Las Vegas is not too crazy about it.

The MGM Grand holds the title as the largest hotel in the world. Now how many elevators would you expect a hotel like this to have? Try 93! With all those elevators, you would think there's always one sitting at the ground floor just waiting to take you to your room. Nope. You have to push that little square button at least three times, after everyone else has pushed it, and only then will one open at the farthest end away from you, where everyone else is standing.

Before there were the plush casinos in Las Vegas that we know today, there were "clubs." They were called clubs because they were not part of a hotel. In fact, in those early days of the '20s and '30s, the few hotels in Las Vegas were rather humble structures because there were few travelers passing through town to use them. There was simply no point in matching the clubs with the hotels. And those clubs were not all that great, either, because most of their trade was "local." But make no mistake, many of those clubs had gaming... *illegal* gaming.

Two of the earliest clubs were the Boulder Club, which opened in downtown Las Vegas in 1929, and the Pair-O-Dice Club on the Los Angeles Highway, now the famed Las Vegas Strip.

In 1931, the year that gaming was legalized in Nevada, The Meadows would become the first true hotel/casino when it opened on Boulder Highway. But it would be ten years later when the El Rancho Vegas opened on the Los Angeles Highway that a "destination" resort attracting visitors from Southern California would set the pace for things to come.

As a footnote, the Boulder Club burned to the ground in 1956, and the land became part of what is now Binion's Horseshoe. The Pair-O-Dice Club was remodeled into the 91 Club (The Los Angeles Highway was actually U.S. 91), and later demolished to make way for the Last Frontier. The Meadows had a short run, but the El Rancho Vegas survived until 1960 when a mysterious fire returned it to its sand and sagebrush beginnings, directly across the Strip from where the Sahara Hotel now stands.

There are more churches in Las Vegas, per capita, than in any other city in the U.S. Over 65 religious faiths are represented in more than 500 churches. No, the churches don't have neon signs. It would seem as if the "Sin City" stigma is a bit out of touch with reality. Tourists only see the glitz and sometimes the gaudy aspects of Las Vegas, but there is a real city there just like yours, made up of hard-working people who are proud to call Las Vegas their home.

Many Las Vegas visitors today can remember the old Castaways Hotel & Casino, although most would remember only the casino... the hotel was rather inconspicuous. But few visitors today would remember the Sans Souci, which is what the Castaways was known as when it opened in 1958. The Castaways had a legendary sports book run by Sonny Reizner, who would set the standard for race and sports books to come.

The property was taken over by Howard Hughes in 1971, and then by Steve Wynn in 1987. But Wynn had no intention of running it. He picked this spot for the location of his Mirage Hotel. It would be most fitting if the sports book at the Mirage would pay tribute to what had stood before it.

Believe it or not, one of the casino's oldest games is now becoming its fastest-growing. The '90s in Las Vegas witnessed an unusual change in a typical casino's floor-plan. At first, more and more blackjack tables were removed to make way for more slot machines. In fact, slot machines had taken over what used to be lounges and bars and even restaurants. Casino executives quickly realized that slots could produce more profit per square foot of gaming space than any other game.

A bigger surprise to gaming operators, however, was the flattening out of interest in blackjack, a game that had made its mark in the late '60s with the introduction of "card-counting." But casino counter-measures over the years had toughened the game so much that newcomers were getting the message: The game *used* to be good.

Indeed. What beckoned the new table-game players was craps. How could they miss the excitement? Everyone at the dice tables seemed to be having all the fun! Now, craps has really caught on. Once players realized how simple the game is, and how low some of the bets are percentage-wise, it was an obvious choice.

But East-coast players already knew this. When Atlantic City casinos first opened in 1978, it was not unusual to find over two-dozen dice tables going full-blast as casinos opened one after another. It was a time when a typical Las Vegas casino might have had four tables, but only one or two actually open for play. By the '90s, however, a game that had its biggest draw in the East was making inroads in the West.

If you're new to Las Vegas, you should be warned about two things: Percentages and tokes. Both can put a big dent in your wallet. You must know that all game percentages are tipped toward the house. Otherwise, how do you suppose they build these palatial palaces? Sure. You know that. You're going to be careful. But what about tips, or *tokes,* as they're known in Vegas? It seems that every time you turn around, someone has their hand out.

It's not unusual for some regular visitors to establish two different budgets when they come to Las Vegas: a budget for gambling and a budget for tipping. Ludicrous, you say? Well, here's the scoop: The hotel operators in Las Vegas very much appreciate your subsidizing their huge payrolls. Here's what they recommend: Two dollars per day for the maid, one dollar per towel for the pool attendant, and two dollars per chaise lounge. Another two dollars every time your car is picked up from valet (tip when it's picked up, not dropped off). Two dollars per bag when you check in (that's for the bellman; it doesn't include a dollar a bag for the doorman to watch your bags until the bellman gets there). Food servers expect 20 percent of the tab whether the service is good or not. Showroom maitre d's will put you in the back row if you don't shake their hand with at least a ten-spot in between.

Taxi drivers, tour guides, change persons, and restroom attendants are on the tip-list, too. But on top of the list are DEALERS. Here's where you can go crazy if you're not careful. Heed these rules: Tip only when you win. Tip only at the end of a playing session. Tip only when dealers have been friendly. And never tip by making a bet for dealers. They don't want to gamble. They know all about gambling. They want the moola. A hundred-dollar win is worth a five-dollar chip. A thousand in your pocket is worth twenty-five in theirs.

Forget the budget, just tip what you think is fair... for good service!

Las Vegas is said to have more cellular phones per capita than any other city in the U.S. It seems as if everyone has a phone stuck to their ear. "Uh, Bob, this is Harry. I've got a 16, the dealer's showing a 6. I forgot, do I hit it or stand?"

Have you ever tried to describe a Las Vegas hotel to someone who has never been there? You can probably get away with a few, but don't try it with the Venetian. If a picture is worth a thousand words, the Venetian has a thousand pictures. The incredible replica of St. Mark's Square is overwhelming. The canals of Venice are a romantic dream. It is an all-suite hotel for connoisseurs of life's *largest* pleasures.

Would you enjoy walking into a Las Vegas casino... in the '50s? Would you like to do that today? Yes, I know, time machines haven't been invented yet, but I can get you there today. OK, maybe not a casino, but how about a showroom?

Most nostalgia buffs who love Las Vegas would probably pick the old Desert Inn as the place they would most love to visit in the '50s, and that's just the place I have in mind.

You see, since Wilbur Clark built the DI in 1950, it has undergone three major renovations: in 1963, 1979, and 1997. You would expect that nothing remains from the early days, and you would be wrong. Somehow, the architects and builders over-looked the DI's Crystal Showroom. Walk in the next time you're in town, close your eyes, and pretend that the Don Arden Dancers are on stage just to entertain *you*. The showroom is rarely locked during the day. Go ahead. Take a trip back in time. But hurry.

Another renovation can't be far behind. After all, this is Vegas.

Although it doesn't happen very often, Las Vegas blackjack bosses can exclude card-counters; they can ask them to leave the game, but they can't make them leave the casino. Many players seem confused about this. They might be thinking about the rules and regs in Atlantic City, and other new gaming venues, where card-counters must be permitted to play, but under some rather tough playing conditions. Vegas takes a different approach.

If you're thinking about becoming a card-counter, here's a fact about blackjack that few players know: If you try to count the cards in a 6-deck or 8-deck shoe, you are probably wasting your time. All those cards virtually eliminate the major fluctuations in your count that you're looking for, and greatly reduce the benefits of end-play (the last few hands) particularly when one-and-a-half to two decks are removed from play by a deeply positioned cut-card.

But a single or double deck is different. You can bet your last dollar that the bosses are watching these tables a lot more closely than the multiple-deck shoes. If they suspect you are counting—and winning—it's more likely they will tell the dealer to "shuffle up." A premature shuffle takes away any advantage you might have had. Besides, it's a nicer way to handle the situation, and most casino bosses in Las Vegas agree.

It's a fact. Craps is easy to play. It only *looks* complicated. I'm going to prove to you that craps is easy. I'm only going to spend one paragraph teaching you the basic game. Are you ready?

Once a win-lose decision has been made, the next roll of the dice is called a "come-out." Put a $5 chip on the pass-line, directly in front of you, and let's play. A 7 or 11 wins. A 2, 3, or 12 loses. Any other number—called "point-numbers"—4, 5, 6, 8, 9, or 10, must be repeated before a 7 is rolled in order to win. Now, if the shooter did indeed throw a point-number, put $10 directly behind your pass-line bet. This is called a double-odds bet. It pays off at the true odds of making the point-number before a 7. The point-numbers 4 or 10 pay 2 to 1 (your odds bet will win $20), the point-numbers 5 or 9 pay 3 to 2 (your odds bet will win $15), the point-numbers 6 or 8 pay 6 to 5 (your odds bet will win $12). The nickel on the pass-line, incidentally, wins at even money... $5 wins $5. That's it. That's all you need to know to get your feet wet. Jump in.

Are you familiar with the Stratosphere Tower? You can't miss it; you can see it from everywhere.

Are you into really getting the you-know-what scared out of you? Yeah? Then let me tell you about it.

It's 1,149 feet high, which makes it the tallest free-standing observation tower in the U.S. And it's the tallest building west of the Mississippi. This thing just plain belongs in Vegas.

Someone had the idea of building a roller coaster on the very top of it. I don't know who he is, but he needs to be checked out. Anyhow, It's called "High Roller." Cute, huh? And as if that's not enough, there's another "ride" called the "Big Shot," which shoots you straight up in the air while your stomach rides about ten feet below you. And speaking of your stomach, there's a revolving restaurant up there, too. In fact, there's at least a couple of places to eat.

Heed my advice: Eat *after* you ride these things.

Here's great news! Are you tired of those long flights to Vegas, and putting up with the airlines... lost luggage, delayed flights, and cramped seats... and then screwing around with a rental car company that lost your reservation? Or, if you drive to Vegas, those five-hour drives have got to be getting on your nerves, right? Screaming kids in the back seat, idiot drivers who cut you off, grandpa going all of 40 miles an hour right in front of you, and two semis hogging the left lane. There's got to be a better way to get there. Well, now there is!

Just call the Las Vegas Hilton and tell them you want to be beamed over. That's right. They have the technology. Seventy-million dollars worth. Hilton collaborated with Paramount to "go where no man has gone before." It's call "Star Trek: The Experience." Once you get there, though, there's a downside to all this. Each visitor has to dress up like a Starfleet officer, or an alien if you're that type, and do a little role-playing on the deck of the U.S.S. Enterprise.

But of all the neat stuff they've got, the Transporter room is where it's at. The Hilton says they can beam over a family of four from Crocket's Bluff, Arkansas, for only $59.95! Not bad, huh? The price even includes a free buffet in the Cardassian Restaurant.

The pyramid design of the Luxor Hotel creates a huge atrium in the center of this imposing structure. Rumor has it that nine Boeing 747s could be stacked one on top of another. Of course, this is only a theory; no one has actually tried it.

Since each floor of the Luxor Hotel is stepped inward as the pyramid rises, it's fun getting to your guest room. The elevators do not go straight up; they rise at a rather steep 29 degree angle. Of course, they are not called elevators; they are *inclinators*.

When the Luxor was giving tours through ancient Egyptian tombs, there were ancient coins scattered everywhere. But these coins, of course, were just replicas. Counterfeit coins to be sure. But in the gift shop, after the tour, visitors could buy real ones! That's right, 5,000-year-old coins were for sale! I think I'd rather take a tour of the gift shop!

What does Las Vegas have more of than any other city? No, not hookers. Casinos for sure. Celebrities, too. It's been said that at any given time, there are more famous faces in Vegas than in Hollywood! And what about cash? Do you want to guess how many C-notes are floating around Vegas? A hundred-dollar bill is the standard monetary unit in Las Vegas. People buy Big Macs with a "bill" and buy cars with a suitcase full of them. It's the only town in America where car dealers all have big safes to keep the tens of thousands of dollars they get every day in hundred-dollar bills.

But what Vegas also has, that few other big cities have, is *rooms*. Get this: There are now over 125,000 rooms available for you to choose from. Should be easy, right? Well, how many times have you called to get a room and the girl in the reservations department says, "We don't have any." So you call another hotel and you're told, "We don't have any." So you argue and argue, and someone finally puts you in touch with a motel halfway between Searchlight and Winnemucca, where the first thing you see is some guy walking around who looks an awful lot like Anthony Perkins.

Here's a valuable list for you to keep with you. The biggest hotels are listed, along with their phone numbers and the number of rooms. Now you've got some ammunition. But for these places, you'll need a thick roll of hundred-dollar bills, too. The list is the top 13 hotels in Las Vegas (I like lucky numbers), based on the number of rooms. And just to show you how big these hotels are, they are not just the biggest in Vegas, they are the biggest in America!

THE LARGEST HOTELS IN THE UNITED STATES

RANK	HOTEL NAME	TOLL-FREE	LOCAL*	ROOMS
1	MGM Grand	800-929-1111	891-1111	5,005
2	Luxor	800-288-1000	262-4000	4,467
3	Excalibur	800-937-7777	597-7777	4,008
4	Circus Circus	800-634-3450	734-0410	3,770
5	Flamingo Hilton	800-732-2111	733-3111	3,642
6	Mandalay Bay	877-632-7000	632-7777	3,309
7	Las Vegas Hilton	800-732-7117	732-5111	3,174
8	Mirage	800-627-6667	791-7111	3,044
9	The Venetian	800-494-3556	733-5000	3,036
10	Bellagio	888-987-6667	693-7111	3,005
11	Monte Carlo	800-311-8999	730-7777	3,002
12	Paris Las Vegas	888-266-5687	946-7000	2,916
13	Treasure Island	800-944-7444	894-7111	2,900

*The area code for Las Vegas is 702

Although the Flamingo Hotel was certainly not the first resort in Las Vegas, contrary to popular belief, it was by far the most celebrated. It was built by Benjamin "Bugsy" Siegel, part of the Meyer Lansky mob organization.

The Flamingo had this tacky pink-neon sign out in front and pink flamingos all over the place. Siegel, apparently, had this thing about flamingos. Maybe because "pink" was his favorite color.

After a rush to get it open, following years of construction delays, it all came together on New Year's Eve 1946. But there were problems, not the least of which was a snowstorm in the mountains that prevented many of the celebrities from Hollywood from even getting there.

I should probably mention here that good ol' Bugsy didn't exactly design the resort, nor did he start the construction. The project was well underway before he got involved. The 1992 movie, *Bugsy,* challenged the historical accuracy of the events in those remark-able days, so it's not unusual for some people to get a distorted view of exactly what happened. For one thing, researchers believe that the dealers were poorly trained, costing the hotel thousands of dollars. It was said that customers were taking advantage of the situation by telling the dealers how much to pay them!.

Historians also believe that other preparations for the grand opening were sorely inadequate. There was little organization and too many people in charge. Some things didn't work; other things weren't finished. The hotel soon closed, but would reopen months later.

Needless to say, all of this didn't bode well with the money-people who backed this "crazy idea" of Siegel's. Six months after the Flamingo opened, Siegel was murdered by an unknown gunman who took out the mob's frustrations with a shotgun. Siegel was killed while sitting on a sofa in front of a big picture window in the living room of the Beverly Hills home of his girlfriend, Virginia Hill.

Bugsy had been paranoid about security, even building a special suite for himself at the hotel, with hidden stairways and bulletproof glass. Sadly, the Hilton Corporation, after buying the hotel, removed this fortress-like room to make way for a new tower. There's nothing left of the original Flamingo; even his famous rose garden is gone. It's now a parking lot.

Few Las Vegas visitors have ever heard of the Moulin Rouge Hotel & Casino, built away from the Strip in 1955, at a time when black entertainers, as well as black guests, were not welcome at other hotels.

It had its ups and downs when it opened. But when Joe Louis, the late heavyweight champion of the world, became an owner of the hotel, it looked promising. After putting his heart and soul into the business, even the "Brown Bomber" couldn't make it last the 12 rounds. The Moulin Rouge finally went down for the count, never again to reopen. Louis moved over to Caesars Palace, where he became a cherished friend to thousands of players. The property where the Moulin Rouge stood was declared a national historic site in 1992.

What's your sign? No, I mean your favorite sign. Your favorite Las Vegas sign. For nearly 30 years, the answer was easy: The Golden Nugget. Throughout the '60s and '70s, it was the most photographed sign in Las Vegas. So what do you do when you have such a famous Vegas icon sitting on top of your casino? Why, if you're Steve Wynn, you take it down. It was a bold move in 1984 that didn't sit well with Vegas nostalgia buffs, or even with some city leaders. But to remodel the Golden Nugget into downtown's most lavish casino, the sign just had to go.

On the Strip, the answer isn't as easy. The Stardust claims to have the most photographed sign today, but what about the Riviera, the Flamingo Hilton, and the Rio? For many years, the Sahara boasted of having the world's tallest, free-standing sign. It should be; it's 23 stories high!

The Rio is said to have the most neon, and always seems to win the "Best Of Vegas" poll every year.

But the Stardust is in the running, too. It definitely has the most animation, with 26 different lighting sequences, which makes it tough to take its picture! It just won't stand still!

So do we count all the neon on the building, or just on the sign? No one, apparently, wants to measure the (literally) miles of neon to see who wins.

Lucky The Clown at Circus Circus wins the heavyweight division, weighing in at 120 tons, the heaviest sign in town.

During the '80s, a trend was underway to use more incandescent bulbs to light up the signs, and the effect was startling. You can still see many of them today. There are literally millions of bulbs. They flash, they change color, and... they burn out. And that was the problem. The signs didn't look so hot when a few hundred out of a few thousand checked out early. How would you like to be the guy who has to change all those bulbs on a sign 70 feet up in the air?

Today, bulbs are out. Neon is in. It lasts forever and a day.

The TV show "Vega$" showcased the Desert Inn's $50 million renovation in 1979. The series premiered in 1978, but really took off when ace-detective Dan Tanna started getting all these calls on his car phone (pretty hip for 1979) from Bea, his secretary—best described as every guy's dream for the

reception desk—telling him to meet so-and-so at the
DI. But the real star of the show was that red '57
T-bird with the personal license plate that read:
TANNA.

The glory days of Vegas still live in the movies,
with priceless scenes inside the casinos and on the
Strip. Jane Russell and Victor Mature starred in *The
Las Vegas Story* in 1952. Dan Dailey and Cyd
Charisse were the stars in MGM's great musical,
Meet Me In Las Vegas. But the best casino interiors
are found in *Ocean's 11*. It's the Rat Pack in action,
concocting a scheme to knock off five of the major
casinos. Can they pull it off? The movie, filmed in
1960, can still hold your attention, though there might
be a chuckle here and there.

Gamblers driving up Interstate 15 from Southern
California, particularly those who are anxious to settle
in with a slot machine or sidle up to a blackjack table,
have to force themselves to stay on the road if it's
Vegas they're heading to. Just beyond the California/
Nevada stateline is a town called Primm (it used to be
called Stateline), and thar be casinos there! Three
major casinos: Whiskey Pete's, Primm Valley, and
Buffalo Bills, do tend to lure you off the busy interstate, and that's what the MGM Grand-owned casinos
are hoping for.

If those diehard gamblers drive on by, they have another tough test awaiting them about 20 miles outside of Las Vegas. That's right. Another shot at the jackpot for those who can't wait, and it's an easy-on, easy-off interchange with plenty of parking. The town is called "Jean," and there are two major casinos: Gold Strike and Nevada Landing.

But how many undisciplined gamblers do you suppose there are, limping into Vegas without a penny in their pockets? These "early bird" casinos in the desert know how important it is to be first on the list. But it cuts both ways. They're last on the list on the gamblers' way home! Without a penny in their pockets.

The builders of Paris Las Vegas managed to bring over everything that is Paris... except the attitude. All the major landmarks are re-created in impeccable detail, highlighted by the 50-story Eiffel Tower where you can travel on a glass elevator to an observation deck for a breath-taking view of the Las Vegas Valley. On the way down, there's a little, out-of-the-way French restaurant that the *real* Paris doesn't have. Paris Las Vegas is connected to Bally's to the north by an extension of Rue del la Paix district, a quaint street lined with shops that sell some of the most expensive stuff you've ever seen in your life!

Both properties are owned by Park Place Entertainment.

The decade of top entertainers in Las Vegas was definitely the '60s. And the hotel that got the lion's share of the action was the Sands. Much of the thanks goes to New York club owner Jack Entratter who had the contacts to bring every top-name performer to the Sands Copa room. And he did.

You can't top Frank Sinatra, Dean Martin, and Sammy Davis Jr. They were the "regulars" at the Sands, often surprising an unknown lounge singer, grabbing the mike and doing a duet that would give the singer something to tell his grandchildren about. Danny Thomas might stop by. Carol Burnett and George Gobel were there. And Joey Bishop, for sure. And when things got crazy, you might find Peter Lawford dealing blackjack, or Red Skelton spinning the ball around the roulette wheel, never quite getting the hang of it.

It was a fun time.

A Caesars Palace press release says that the Brahma Shrine, built near the center Strip entrance to the hotel, is an "authentic replica" of Thailand's most popular Buddhist shrine. Is that an oxymoron, or what? And get this: The original Brahma Shrine was installed to ward off bad luck. Now I ask you: Does

Caesars Palace really want this thing at the front of its hotel, where all the players enter on their way in to test their luck?! If that thing really works, Caesars may have to invest in black cats!

Who can forget the build-up to Evel Knievel's death-defying jump over the towering row of fountains at Caesars Palace? It happened on December 31, 1967, a date Knievel would probably like to forget. But on April 14, 1989, in front of a national television audience and 50,000 excited fans gathered at the hotel, Evel's son, Robbie, avenged his father's failure by performing a flawless jump into stardom, not to mention *Las Vegas Trivia*.

Other Great Gambling Titles
From Gollehon Books

Budget Gambling

Conquering Casino Craps

Casino Gambling For Winners

A Gambler's Bedside Reader

Casino Gambling Behind The Tables

What Casinos Don't Want You To Know

The Confident Gambler

Gambling's Greatest Hits

A Gambler's Little Instruction Book

The Book Casino Managers Fear The Most

Slot Machine Mania

Video Poker Mania

Beat The Track

Casino Games

Casino Comics